D1604087

DETROIT STUDIES

IN

MUSIC BIBLIOGRAPHY

GENERAL EDITOR

BRUNO NETTL

UNIVERSITY OF ILLINOIS AT URBANA-CHAMPAIGN

ON THE COVER AND AT RIGHT
The organ built in 1697 by
Arp Schnitger at Groningen,
Onze Lieve-Vrouw or *Aa-Kerk*.
FROM A DRAWING ASCRIBED TO SCHNITGER

FOUR CENTURIES OF ORGAN MUSIC

From the Robertsbridge Codex through the Baroque Era

An Annotated Discography

Marilou Kratzenstein
and
Jerald Hamilton

DETROIT STUDIES IN MUSIC BIBLIOGRAPHY NUMBER FIFTY-ONE
INFORMATION COORDINATORS 1984 DETROIT

Printed and bound in the United States of America
Published by
Information Coordinators, Inc.
1435-37 Randolph Street
Detroit, Michigan 48226

Editing by J. Bunker Clark, University of Kansas
Book design by Vincent Kibildis
Photocomposition by Joy P. Hick

Library of Congress Cataloging in Publication Data
Kratzenstein, Marilou, 1937-
Four centuries of organ music.
(Detroit studies in music bibliography ; no. 51)
Bibliography: p.
Includes indexes.
1. Organ music—Discography.
I. Hamilton, Jerald, 1927-   . II. Title.
III. Title: 4 centuries of organ music.
IV. Series: Detroit studies in music bibliography ; 51.
ML156.4.06K7 1984   016.7899'1265   84-546
ISBN 0-89990-020-8

Contents

Contents

Preface

Since the present discography has grown out of the compilers' need to identify recordings of organ music particularly useful as illustrative material for undergraduate and graduate courses in organ literature, both the character and arrangement of the work have been determined primarily by such a presentation.

Subsequent considerations have resulted in our confining the survey to the period beginning with the Robertsbridge Codex and concluding with the end of the Baroque era. While we have included a few discs issued on private labels, we have chosen in principle to limit ourselves to commercial recordings that fall both within the given time frame and within the other limits of our study. Although a few recordings made at 45 rpm have been included, we have been concerned basically with those at 33⅓ rpm.

The year 1750 was chosen as an approximate cut-off date, with some allowance made for organ music in Baroque style composed after this date. Anthologies that contain compositions of the nineteenth or twentieth centuries in addition to earlier music have been included only if a major portion antedates 1750.

We have further generally limited ourselves to recordings that appeared between 1970 and 1980. Older recordings have been included only if 1) they are still listed in publishers' or distributors' catalogs, 2) they are still commonly to be found in music libraries, or 3) the performer, instrument, or record series is of singular importance for the repertory performed.

Newer recordings from the 1981 and 1982 Musical Heritage Society catalogs were added during a recent revision of the manuscript. In addition, a few entries that had lately come to our attention were also incorporated at the time of publication. These added items were assigned four-digit decimal numbers (e.g., 263.1) to avoid renumbering the entire discography.

Preface

Entries have been grouped in chapters devoted respectively to the Late Medieval, Renaissance, and Baroque periods. Since no recordings dealing exclusively with the Late Medieval period could be found, the entries consist of anthologies that combine Late Medieval music with that of the Renaissance and/or Baroque. Some of these recordings are for organ alone; others feature instrumental or vocal ensembles with organ.

Within the chapters on the Renaissance and Baroque, entries are arranged first by country of origin. For each country, anthologies containing works of more than one composer are listed first; following the anthologies is a section of recordings of the works of individual composers, arranged in alphabetical order. To conclude both the Renaissance and Baroque, we have listed anthologies of mixed national origin whose contents could not be subsumed under one of the designated categories. In such a case, and in the case of recordings that span two or more designated historical periods, a main listing and one or more secondary cross listings will be found.

The very large number of recordings of the organ music of J. S. Bach has suggested the need for further subdivisions in arrangement of entries. Recordings of the complete organ works are listed first. After this is a section of the chorale-based works, with recordings of each of the several collections listed separately (e.g., *Clavierübung* Part III, Leipzig Chorales, etc.). At the end of the section of chorale-based works is a listing of recordings of mixed categories. The free works, in turn, are similarly subdivided, with, again, a section of mixed categories at the end. Finally, the section on J. S. Bach is concluded with an extensive listing of anthologies which include both chorale-based and free works. Throughout the Bach listings, in order both to abbreviate as much as possible and, where necessary, to avoid possible confusion between works of the same title and key, the Schmieder (BWV) numbering has been used. A summary list of the Bach organ works according to the Schmieder catalog may be found in the appendix.

Throughout the discography each entry is listed, within its appropriate category, in alphabetical order according to the surname of the performer. Where two or more performers are included in a given entry, the recording is arranged according to the first of the alphabetical surnames. Each entry provides first the surname of the performer(s), then, when known, the title of the recording. Following this information are 1) the name and identification number of the manufacturer, often with supplemental information which identifies reissues on other labels; 2) the date of pressing, when known, indicated in brackets; and 3) the number of discs, if more than one.

Titles of individual compositions, or a summary of the contents, are listed next in alphabetical order of composer. Upper and lower case letters enclosed in parentheses indicate major or minor keys. For the most part, titles in this discography conform to those appearing in catalogs or on the discs or record jackets themselves, although we have permitted ourselves to translate certain titles and to correct some obvious errors. Following the listing of contents, supplemental or explanatory information includes, when available, an identification of the organ(s) according to builder and location.

An asterisk to the left of an entry indicates that the recording was advertised as available for purchase no less recently than 1978. How long each recording will remain available, is, however, impossible to predict.

In the course of our compilation we discovered certain problems to which the reader should be alerted. Record manufacturers are often imprecise in assigning titles to their recordings. They may, for example, list in their catalog a title slightly different from that found on the record jacket. The former may be an abbreviated version of the jacket title, or it may be a description of the record contents. Discrepancies exist frequently also in the manufacturer's identification number. A given recording may be listed by the manufacturer at various times under two or three different numbers. Sometimes the new number indicates a re-pressing of an older recording, or a change from monaural to stereo. At other times it may mean nothing more than that the manufacturer has changed his numbering system. When ordering records, the reader would be well advised to supply as much information as possible.

Acknowledgement is here made to the University of Northern Iowa, which provided a summer research grant which assisted in this project. To the staff of the Music Library of the University of Illinois at Urbana-Champaign, we would like to express particular gratitude for their invaluable help over the extended period during which this discography has been in progress.

MARILOU KRATZENSTEIN
University of Northern Iowa
Cedar Falls

JERALD HAMILTON
University of Illinois
Urbana-Champaign

January 1983

PART ONE

Late Medieval

CHAPTER 1

MIXED NATIONAL ORIGIN

An asterisk to the left
of an entry number indicates
that the recording was advertised
for purchase
as recently as 1978.

Anthologies

BERNARD and HOGWOOD, organ; EARLY MUSIC CONSORT ***1**
OF LONDON, dir. MUNROW. *Instruments of the Middle Ages and*
Renaissance.
Angel SBZ-3810 [1976]. 2 LPs.

Organ works, which constitute a minority of the works in this set, are:
    ANONYMOUS 15TH-CENTURY GERMAN (*Buxheimer Orgelbuch*):
        Min Hertz hat sich ser gefröwet (Haase regal, 1684).
    DA RIMINI: Madrigal "Ay schonsolato de amoroso" (Mander por-
        tative organ with bass rebec).
    PAUMANN: Prelude "Ascensus simplex" from the *Fundamentum*
        organisandi (Haase regal, 1684).
    ROBERTSBRIDGE CODEX: Estampie (Mander positive organ).
    SOTO: Entrada real (organ at Santa María, Daroca).

The other works on these records provide illustrations of the harpsichord,
clavichord, virginals, and numerous types of stringed, woodwind, brass, and
percussion instruments. The organ is also used with other instruments and
voices in various ensembles.

BIGGS. *Historic Organs of Europe: Switzerland.* ***2**
Columbia MS 6855 (formerly ML 6255 and S 72441 [1966]).

    ANONYMOUS: Sit gloria Domini; Orientis partibus; Christo psallat;
        St. Magnus Hymnus.
    BACH: In dulci jubilo; Wer nur den lieben Gott lässt walten.
    CLERAMBAULT: Dialogue en trompette.
    COUPERIN: "Le Trophée"; Fugue on the Kyrie.

DALZA: Pavana alla venetiana.
DUNSTABLE: Agincourt Hymn.
KOTTER: Praeambulum in fa.
LEONINUS: Haec dies.
PAUMANN: Mit ganczem Willen.
PEROTINUS: Motets for "Haec dies."
PURCELL: Chaconne in F.
RAISON: Passacaglia.
TALLIS: Gloria tibi Trinitas; Three Versets from the Te Deum.

Organs:

Late medieval organ (ca. 1380), Sion, rebuilt 1718 by M. Carlen, with pedal added; Pietro and Lorenzo Bernasconi organ (1882), San Pietro sopra Mendrisio; G. F. Schmahl organ (1741-43), village church, Sitzberg (restored by Metzler, 1960-61); J. A. Silbermann organ (1759-61), Arlesheim Cathedral (restored by Metzler, 1959-62).

BOVET. *L'Orgue de Valère.* See **127.**   3

HILDENBRAND. *Die alte Orgel: Orgel der Burgkirche von Sion;*   4
Orgel der Pfarrkirche zu Vouvray. See **790.**

HOGWOOD, organ; EARLY MUSIC CONSORT OF LONDON, dir.   *5
MUNROW. *The Art of Courtly Love.*
Seraphim SIC-6092 [1973]. 3 LPs.

Works performed on organ (only a fraction of the entire contents) are:
ANONYMOUS (14th century): Motet "Tribum quem."
BINCHOIS: Ballade "Jeloymors."
MACHAUT: Ballade "De toutes fleurs."
PIERRE DES MOULINS: Rondeau "Amis tous dous."

The organ is used also as an ensemble instrument in various combinations. The record set as a whole provides a survey of French secular music, both vocal and instrumental, from the time of Machaut to that of Dufay.

JACKSON, N. *The Organ at Adlington Hall.* See **172.**   6

JAQUET. *La Musique d'orgue en Europe du Moyen Age à la*   ***7**
Renaissance.
Arion 38434.

> ANONYMOUS: Estampie and retrové; My Lady Carey's Dompe.
> ATTAINGNANT: Basse danse; Branle gay du Poitou; Gaillardes;
>   Pavane.
> ILEBORGH: 2 preludes.
> NEUSIEDLER: Der zeuner Tanz; Judentantz.
> PAUMANN: Mit ganczem Willen; Quant ien congneu a pa pensée.
> PEROTIN: Deux points d'orgue.
> SCHLICK: Hoe Losteleck; Maria zart. (Additional works not iden-
>   tified.)

Kern organ, modeled after Silbermann, Church of Saint-Jean, Mulhouse.

MUSICA RESERVATA OF LONDON. *The Instruments of the*   ***8**
Middle Ages and Renaissance.
Vanguard VSD 71219/20 [1977]. 2 LPs.

Organ works, which constitute a minority of the works in this set, are:
> ANONYMOUS (16th century): Moneghina Gagliarda (positive organ);
>   Pass' e mezo antico terzo (regal).
> BUCHNER: Dantz Moss Benczenauher (positive organ).
> DE FLORENTIA: Cosa crudel (soprano and portative organ).

The other works on these records provide illustrations of the clavichord, virginal, harpsichord, and numerous types of stringed, woodwind, brass, and percussion instruments.

REICHLING, organ; MARIA LAACH ABTEI chanters;   ***9**
CAPELLA ANTIQUA STUTTGART; AURBACHER, mezzo soprano;
SCHAIBLE, baritone, dir. HOFMANN. *Missa mediaevalis.*
Psallite PSC 38 100 267.

Organ works:
> Two pieces from the *Robertsbridge Codex.*

Other works:
> Mass propers from the Gregorian Christmas mass "Puer natus est."
> Mass ordinary: Barcelona Mass (from the Ars Nova period).

Führer organ, Andernach.

ROGG, positive organ; CLEMENCIC CONSORT, dir. CLEMENCIC; ***10**
ENSEMBLE RICERCARE. *Danses du Moyen-Age.*
Harmonia Mundi HM 2.472. 2 LPs.

Organ works:
> AMMERBACH: Passamezzo.
> ANONYMOUS: Bassa imperiale; Estampie and estampie retrové.
> ASTON: Hornepype.
> ATTAINGNANT: Gaillarde.
> BENDUSI: Cortesana padoana.
> BUXHEIMER ORGELBUCH: Vil lieber Zit; Boumgartner.
> NEUSIEDLER: Judentantz; Der zeuner Tantz.
> SCHMID: Wie schön blüht uns der Maie.

Other works:
> Anonymous instrumental works from the 13th-15th centuries, and instrumental and vocal works of Dufay, Machaut, and Marguerite d'Autriche.

Hartmann positive organ.

ROGG. *Danses, Enigmes, Estampies.*   **11**
Harmonia Mundi HMO 763.

> AMMERBACH: Passamezzo.
> ANONYMOUS (ca. 1350): Estampie and estampie retrové (*Robertsbridge Codex*).
> ANONYMOUS (ca. 1620): Bassa imperiale.
> ASTON: Hornepype.
> ATTAINGNANT: Gaillarde.
> J. S. BACH: Chorale preludes, S. 601, 608; Prelude and Fugue (D), S. 532; Sonata VI.
> BENDUSI: Cortesana padoana.
> BUXHEIMER ORGELBUCH: Vil lieber Zit (Baumgartner).
> BYRD: Alman; Callino custurame.
> FARNABY: Tower Hill.
> NEUSIEDLER: Juden Tanz; Zeuner Tanz.
> SCHMIDT: Wie schön blüht uns der Maie.
> TOMKINS: Short Verse.

Organs:
> 16th-century Swiss table organ; Hartmann positive; J. A. Silbermann organ, Arlesheim (1759-61).

ROGG, positive organ; ENSEMBLE RICERCARE. *Estampies,*   ***12**
Basses danses, Pavanes.
Harmonia Mundi HM 573. 2LPs.

Organ works:
 AMMERBACH: Passamezzo.
 ANONYMOUS: Bassa imperiale; estampie and estampie retrové.
 ASTON: Hornepype.
 ATTAINGNANT: Gaillarde.
 BENDUSI: Cortesana padoana.
 BUCHNER: Ach hülf mich Leif und sehnlich Klag.
 NEUSIEDLER: Judentantz; Der zeuner Tantz.
 SCHMID: Wie schön blüht uns der Maie.

Other works:
 Anonymous instrumental works taken from the publications of Attaingnant (1530), Susato (1551), and Phalese (1571 and 1583).

Hartmann positive.

VAN DER VEN, organ; BRUECKNER-RUEGGEBERG, tenor;   **13**
NUREMBERG GAMBENCOLLEGIUM, dir. ULSAMER. *Fourteen
Lieder and Instrumental Pieces from the Locheimer Liederbuch.*
Deutsche Grammophon (Archive) ARC 3222 [1964].

Organ works:
 PAUMANN: Des klaffers neyden; Mit ganczem willen (from *Fun-
 damentum organisandi*).

Instrumental and vocal works:
 H. SACHS: Als ich, Hans Sachs, alt ware; Gloria Patri; Lob und er;
 Ich lob ein brünnlein küle; Ein Tigertier; Zu Venedig ein kaufman
 sass.
 LOCHEIMER LIEDERBUCH: All mein gedencken dy ich hab; Es fur
 ein pawr gen holz; Ich het mir auszerkoren; Ich spring an disem
 ringe; Ich var dohin; Des klaffers neyden; Mein trawt geselle; Mit
 ganczem willen; Möcht ich dein geberen; Der Summer; Ein vrouleen
 edel von naturen; Der wallt hat sich enlawbet.

NOTE: Although they have not been listed individually, the *History of Music in Sound,*
the *Historical Anthology of Music in Performance,* and the *Treasury of Early Music*
also contain a few examples of organ music.

PART TWO

Renaissance

*An asterisk to the left
of an entry number indicates
that the recording was advertised
for purchase
as recently as 1978.*

Anthologies

BIGGS. *Historic Organs of England.*   ***14**
Columbia M 30445.

> ANONYMOUS: The Agincourt Hymn (melody attributed to
> Dunstable); Packington's Pound; Upon la mi re; Ritornello.
> ASTON: A Hornepype.
> BYRD: A Gigg.
> CLARKE: Ayre.
> DOWLAND: The King of Denmark, His Galliard.
> DUNSTABLE: Composition on a Plainsong.
> HANDEL: Selections from the *Aylesford Pieces.*
> HOLBORN: Allemande.
> PURCELL: A Ground in Gamut.
> STANLEY: A Trumpet Tune; Introduction and Allegro.
> TALLIS: Gloria tibi Trinitas; Iste confessor.
> TYE: A Point.

Bernard Smith organs in Adlington Hall, Cheshire (ca. 1670), and Staunton
Harold, Leicestershire (ca. 1660-70); a copy of an old regal in the possession
of Noel Mander; the George England organ in the Sanson Mansion, Bexley
(Kent) (1776); the "Handel" organ in Great Packington.

DANBY. *English Organs: St. Mary's Rotherhithe.* See **167**.   **15**

DART, organ, harpsichord, clavichord. *Masters of Early English*   **16**
Keyboard Music, 5 vols.
L'Oiseau-Lyre OLS 114/18 [1955-56]. 5 LPs.

11

VOL 1.

Organ works:

> ANONYMOUS 15TH CENTURY: Felix namque.
> BLITHEMAN: Eterne rerum conditor (No. 3).
> GIBBONS: Fancy (a).
> PRESTON (?): Upon la mi re.
> ROBERTSBRIDGE CODEX: Estampie, Retrové.
> TALLIS: Natus est nobis.

Harpsichord and clavichord works by:

> BLOW, BULL, CLARKE, CROFT, FARNABY, GIBBONS, HOOPER, JOHNSON, NEWMAN, ROSEINGRAVE, and ANONYMOUS.

VOL. 2.

Organ works:

> TOMKINS: Clarifica me Pater; Fancy; Voluntary (No. 30).

Harpsichord music by:

> BYRD and TOMKINS.

VOL. 3.

Organ works:

> BULL: Een Kindekin is uns geboren; Prelude and Fantasy on Sol-ut — mi fa sol la; Fantasy (G); Pavan and Galliard "Sinfoniae"; Vexilla regis; Fantasy on "La Guamina"; Prelude and Fantasy on "Laet uns met Herten reyne"; Salve regina; Fantasy on a Theme of Sweelinck.
> LOCKE: 6 voluntaries (*Melothesia*).

VOLS. 4/5.

Harpsichord works by:

> BULL, FARNABY, and GIBBONS.

Snetzler bureau organ (ca. 1760); Goff harpsichord and clavichord (20th c.).

JACKSON, N. *The Organ at Adlington Hall.* See **172.**   **17**

JONES, organ; DART, harpsichord and clavichord; DONINGTON,   **18**
gamba; GOBLE, harpsichord. *Early English Keyboard Music.*
London LL 712/713 [195-?]. 2 LPs.

> ANONYMOUS: The Lord's Masque; The New Noddy.
> BULL: Walsingham Variations; Queen Elizabeth's Pavan; King's Hunt.

BYRD: Carman's Whistle; Earle of Salisbury's Pavan and Galliard;
   Pavan and Galliard Bray; Preludium.
FARNABY: Wooddy-Cock.
GIBBONS: 2 Fantasies; Lord Salisbury's Pavan and Galliard.
PHILIPS: Pavana dolorosa; Galliarda dolorosa.
TOMKINS: Pavan.

KANN, organ; LONDON AMBROSIAN SINGERS, dir.   ***19**
McCARTHY. *Madrigals and Keyboard Music of the English Renaissance.*
Musical Heritage Society 1173.

Organ works:
   ANONYMOUS: I smile to see how you devise; The Maiden's Song; O
      ye happy dames; Since thou art false to me.
   BLITHEMAN: Eterne rerum alias, IV.
   CARLETON: Gloria tibi Trinitas.
   EDWARDS: When griping griefs.
   REDFORD: Christe qui lux est; Eterne rex altissime; Glorificamus; Iam
      lucis orto sidere; O Lux with a Meane; Salvator with a Meane; [un-
      titled piece].
   SHELBYE: Miserere.
   TALLIS: Iste confessor; Per haec nos; A Point; Remember not, O
      Lord.
   TYE: When that the first day was come.

Vocal music:
   Madrigals by BYRD, DOWLAND, GIBBONS, MORLEY, TOMKINS, and
   WEELKES.

Organ music on this recording is from the *Mulliner Book*. Positive organ
designed by E. E. Schuster.

LANDALE. *L'Encyclopédie de l'orgue.* Vol. 41: *L'Orgue anglais*   **20**
des XVIe, XVIIe et XVIIIe siècles. See **173**.

LEONHARDT. *Organ Music of Elizabethan England.*   ***21**
Cambridge CRS 2510.

   BULL: Gloria tibi Trinitas.
   BYRD: Fantasia (*Fitzwilliam Virginal Book* II, 406); Miserere (*FVB*
      II, 232).

FARNABY: Fantasia (*FVB* II, 270); Loth to depart (*FVB* II, 317).
GIBBONS: 2 Fantasias (*Musica Britannica* XX, 7, 11); Prelude (*MB* XX, 6).
MUNDY: Robin.
PHILIPS: Fantasia (*FVB* I, 335).

Schnitger organ, St. Michael's, Zwolle.

Review:

Organ Yearbook 7 (1976): 173.

PAYNE, organ and harpsichord. *A Comprehensive Selection* ∗22
from the Fitzwilliam Virginal Book.
Vox VBX 72 and SVBX 572 [1965]. 3 LPs.

ANONYMOUS: Alman; Barafostus' dream; Can shee; Coranto; Watkin's Ale; Why aske you; Muscadin.
BULL: The Duchesse of Brunswick's Toye; The Duke of Brunswick's Alman; In Nomine.
BYRD: Alman; The Carman's Whistle; 2 Fantasias; A Gigg; Miserere; Monsieurs Alman; Pavana; Pavana and Galliarda; La Volta; A Wolsey's Wilde.
FARNABY: Bonny sweet Robin; Fantasia; Farnabyes Conceit; Giles Farnaby's Dream; His Rest; Loth to Depart; Tower Hill; A Toye; Fayne would I wed.
GIBBONS: Pavana.
JOHNSON: 3 Almans.
MUNDY: Goe from my window; Mundy's Joy.
PEERSON: The Fall of the Leafe.
PHILIPS: Pavana; Pavana dolorosa.

Fisk organ (1964), King's Chapel, Boston.

PETER, organ; LONDON AMBROSIAN SINGERS, dir. ∗23
McCARTHY.
Musical Heritage Society 1526/27. 2 LPs.

Organ works:

ALWOOD: In nomine
ANONYMOUS: (16th c.): Prelude.
REDFORD: Lucem tuam; Te Deum.
TALLIS: Veni Redemptor.
TOMKINS: A Short Verse.

Choral works by:

> BYRD, SMITH, GIBBONS, STONE, WEELKES, TALLIS, TOMKINS,
> TAVERNER, MUNDY, and WHYTE.

Unidentified positive organ.

ROSE and WULSTON, organ; CHOIR OF MAGDALEN   ***24**
COLLEGE, OXFORD, dir. ROSE. *English Polyphonic Church Music.*
Saga XID 5287 and STXID 5287. (Also Audiovision Developments AVM
009.)

Organ works:

> CARLETON: A Verse for Two to Play.
> GIBBONS: Fantasia (a).
> TALLIS: Ex more docti mistico.
> TOMKINS: Pavan.

Choral works by:

> BYRD, DEERING, GIBBONS, MUDD, NICOLSON, SHEPPARD,
> TOMKINS, and ANONYMOUS.

WHITE, organ; CHOIR OF ST. JOHN'S COLLEGE, CAMBRIDGE,   **25**
dir. GUEST. *Tallis and Weelkes: Tudor Church Music.*
Argo ZRG 5237 [1961].

Organ works:

> ANONYMOUS: Voluntary.
> TALLIS: Iam lucis; Clarifica me; Fantasy.
> WEELKES: Voluntary.

Choral works by:

> TALLIS and WEELKES.

Individual Composers

Bull, John

CAMERON, organ; JEANS, virginal; JOHANNES KOCH GAMBA   **26**
CONSORT. *High Renaissance* series: *The Elizabethan Era—John Bull.*
Deutsche Grammophon (Archive) 198 472 SAPM.

Organ works:

In Nomine XII; Dorick music, 4 parts; Fantasia; Te lucis ante ter-
minum; Pavan Symphony; Galliard Symphony; Germans Almaine;
Carol: Den lustelijcken meij; Bull's Goodnight.

Works for virginal and gamba consort.

Joest Siborgh (1642)/Ahrend and Brunzema (1960) organ in Westerhusen
near Emden (Ostfriesland). 16th-century Italian virginal.

Byrd, William

MAYNARD, organ and harpsichord. *Works of Byrd.*   **27**
Decca DL 10040 and 711040 [1961].

The Bagpipe and the Drone; The Carman's Whistle; A Fancie; Fantasia; The Flute and the Droome; French Coranto No. 2; John come
kiss me now; Miserere; Mr. Bird's Upon a Plainesong; Pavan "Earl
of Salisbury"; Pavan and Galliard No. 10; Pavan and Galliarde of
Mr. Birde; Pavane and Galliarde of Mr. Peter; Pipers Galliarde; Ut,
re, mi, fa, sol, la; A Voluntarie.

Holtkamp organ (1957), General Theological Seminary, New York City; Hub-
bard harpsichord (1960).

JESSON, organ; SALTIRE SINGERS. *Works of Byrd.*   ***28**
Musical Heritage Society 877. (Duplicates Lyrichord LLST 7156.)

Organ works:

A Gigg; Miserere; Pavan and Galliard; Praeludium.

Vocal works:

Madrigals, motets, and anthems.

Gibbons, Orlando

HOGWOOD, organ, harpsichord, and spinet. *Orlando Gibbons:*   ***29**
Keyboard Music.
L'Oiseau-Lyre DSLO 515.

Organ works:

Fancy; 2 Fantasias; Fantasia of four parts; Verse.

Works for harpsichord or spinet.

Bernard Smith cabinet organ.

PRESTON, organ; JACOBEAN CONSORT OF VIOLS; CHOIR OF   ***30**
KING'S COLLEGE, CAMBRIDGE, dir. WILLCOCKS. *Sacred Music:*
Music for Matins and Verse Anthems.
Argo ZK8 (formerly ZRG 5151 [1959]).

Organ works:
Voluntaries I and II.
Vocal works:
Anthems and service music.

Tallis, Thomas

DAVIS and LANGDON, organ; CHOIR OF KING'S COLLEGE,   ***31**
CAMBRIDGE; CAMBRIDGE UNIVERSITY MUSICAL SOCIETY
CHORUS, dir. WILLCOCKS. *Tudor Church Music,* vols. 1 and 2.
Argo ZK 30/31 [1965/66]. 2 LPs. (Formerly issued as ZRG 5436 and 5479.)

VOL. 1.
Organ works:
Ecce tempus; Veni Redemptor.
Vocal works:
Latin motets.

VOL. 2.
Organ works:
Organ Lesson.
Vocal works:
Motets, etc.

Tomkins, Thomas

GOWER, organ; CHOIR OF MAGDALEN COLLEGE, OXFORD,   ***32**
dir. ROSE. *Thomas Tomkins: Church Music.*
Decca 682 (a reissue of Argo ZRG 249 [1961]).

Organ works:
Voluntary; A Fancy for Two to Play.
Vocal works:
Anthems and service music.

SIDWELL, organ; IN NOMINE PLAYERS; THE AMBROSIAN   **33**
SINGERS, dir. STEVENS. *Music of the 16th and 17th Centuries,*
vol. 5: *Thomas Tomkins,* part 1.
Musical Heritage Society 687. (Duplicates Experiences Anonymes EA-0027
[1957].)

Organ works:
   3 voluntaries (C, D, a).

Vocal works:
   Anthems and service music.

Snetzler chamber organ (1796).

Anthologies

CHAPUIS, organ; ENSEMBLE VOCAL CAILLAT. *L'Orgue de*   **34**
Saint-Séverin, Paris.
Harmonia Mundi 570.

Organ works:
    TITELOUZE: Exsultet coelum; Pange lingua; Veni Creator; Ave maris
    stella; Magnificat.

Choral works:
    Polyphonic versets by J. DE BOURNONVILLE, E. DU CAURROY, and
    N. FORME.

Héman (1626)/Thierry/Kern organ, St. Séverin, Paris.

CHAPUIS, organ; DELLER CONSORT.   ***35**
Harmonia Mundi HMU 251.

Organ works:
    TITELOUZE: Veni Creator.

Choral works:
    LE JEUNE: Missa "Ad placitum."

Héman (1626)/Thierry/Kern organ, St. Séverin, Paris.

DARASSE and ISOIR. *16th-Century French Organ Music.*   ***36**
Turnabout TV 34126 S.

19

ATTAINGNANT: Suite of Dances; Chanson; L'Espoir que j'ay.
TITELOUZE: Ave maris stella; Urbs Jerusalem; Exsultet coelum; Ad coenam.

Isoir regal organ; Clicquot organ (1717), Cathedral of Sarlat, Dordogne; Héman/Thierry/Kern organ, St. Séverin, Paris.

DARASSE, ISOIR, and TERRASSE. *A Survey of the World's*   *37
Greatest Organ Music: France, vol. 1 — *"The Primitives."*
Vox SVBX 5310. 3 LPs.

RECORD ONE.

ANONYMOUS (Attaingnant): L'Espoir que j'ay; Suite of dances; 3 Versets on the Te Deum; Prelude to the 13 motets; Magnificat on the 4th Tone; Kyrie cunctipotens.
ANONYMOUS (16th c.): Quant ien congneu a pa pensée; Variations on the Kyrie cunctipotens.
COSTELEY: Fantasy.
DE SERMISY: Motet "Si bona suscipemus"; Secourez moy.
DU CAURROY: Fantasy on "Ave maris stella"; Fantasy in 5 parts on "Une jeune Fillette."
GUILLET: Third Fantasy.
JANNEQUIN: Aller my fault.
LE JEUNE: Second fantasy.
PEROTIN LE GRAND: Organum triplex.

RECORD TWO.

RACQUET: Two duets; Fantasy.
TITELOUZE: Ave maris stella; Urbs Jerusalem; Exsultet coelum; Ad coenam.

RECORD THREE.

DUMONT: Allemande grave; Prélude; Pavane; Courante; Allemande.
ROBERDAY: Fugues I, II, III, VI, VIII.

Organs in the Cathedral of Sarlat and in St. Séverin, Paris. See **36**.

ISOIR. *Le Livre d'or de l'orgue français,* vol. 1: *L'Orgue à la*   *38
Renaissance.
Calliope 1.901.

ANONYMOUS: Basse danse; Branle; L'espoir que j'ay; Gaillardes; Kyrie cunctipotens; Magnificat du 4e ton; Prélude; Tant que vivray; 3 versets du Te Deum.

SCHNEIDER: Adagio con affetto.
SICHER: In dulci jubilo; Resonet in laudibus.
SPETH: Magnificat quinti toni.

Side five includes 2 canzoni by HASSLER. The remaining literature in this volume is from the Baroque and Classical eras. For the continuation of this volume, see **388**.

Egedacher (1686)/Jäger (1780) organ, Benedictine Monastery, Upper Bavaria; Sandtner (20th c.) organ, St. Martinskirche, Jettingen; Daum organ (1723), St. Laurentiuskirche, Meeder.

LEHRNDORFER. *Hoforganisten aus vier Jahrhunderten.*   **53**
See **148**.

MAURISCHAT. *Pape-Orgeldokumente,* vol. 9: *Orgel der ev.-*   ***54**
luther. Kirche in Hohenkirchen/Jeverland.
Fono Schallplatten Münster 63 709 POD.

BUCHNER: Christ ist erstanden; Sancta Maria wohn uns bey.
ISAAC: Herr Gott, lass dich erbarmen; Innsbruck ich muss dich lassen;
    Innsbruck ad equalis.
KOTTER: Praeludium (d); Aus tieffer nodt schry ich zu dir.
LUBLIN: De profundis.
LÜBECK: Präludium (C).
SCHEIDEMANN: In dich habe ich gehoffet, Herr; Praeambulum (g).
SCHLICK: Da pacem, Domine.
WECKMANN: Nun freut euch, lieben Christen g'mein.

Kayser (1694-99)/Führer (1974) organ.

Reviews:
Ars organi 26/55 (February 1978): 310; *Organ Yearbook* 8 (1977):
99-100; *Musik und Kirche* 46/2 (March-April 1976): 89-90.

REICHLING, organ; CAPELLA ANTIQUA STUTTGART, dir.   ***55**
HOFFMAN. *Freudenreiche Weihnachts-Lobgesang* (from the *Ander-*
nacher Gesangbuch, 1608).
Psallite PEU 45/170767.

Organ works:
ANONYMOUS: Präambulum.

ERBACH: Canzon del 6º tono; Intonatio 2^i toni.
SALEM: Resonet in laudibus.
SICHER: Resonet in laudibus.

Vocal works by:

ECCARD, FINCK, PAMINGER, M. PRAETORIUS, WALTER, and
ANONYMOUS.

RILLING. *A Survey of the World's Greatest Organ Music:*   **56**
Germany, vol. 1 — *North Germany.* See **399**.

SACHS, K.-J., and SCHRÖDER. *Musik an der Praetorius-*   **57**
Orgel der Universität Freiburg im Breisgau.
Walcker Stiftung WST-1 [196-?].

FRESCOBALDI: Bergamasca.
KOTTER: Praeludium in fa.
NIKOLAUS VON KRAKAU: Ave hierarchia.
M. PRAETORIUS: Nun lob, mein Seel, den Herren.
SCHEIDEMANN: Magnificat VIII^i toni.
SCHEIDT: Alamanda "Bruynsmedelijn"; Hymnus "Veni Redemptor
    gentium."
SWEELINCK: Echo-Fantasie (d).

Walcker (1954-55) "Praetorius" organ, University of Freiburg; the instrument
built to specifications of W. Gurlitt based on Praetorius, *De Organographia.*

Review:

Organ Yearbook 3 (1972): 116.

SCHNAUFFER. *Historische Orgeln Schwaben.* See **406**.   **58**

TRIEBEL. *Historische Orgeln Steiermark.* See **422**.   **59**

Individual Composers

Praetorius, Michael

DALLMANN. *Complete Organ Works.*   *****60**

Da Camera 93 229/30. 2 LPs. (The two volumes are duplicated by Musical Heritage Society 3993 and 4281.)

Organ at the University of Freiburg. See **57**.

Senfl, Ludwig

LENZ, organ; PÖHLERT RENAISSANCE ENSEMBLE, dir.   ***61**
PÖHLERT. *Ludwig Senfl.*
Musical Heritage Society 1390. (Duplicates Da Camera 91 704.)

Organ works:

> Praeambulum 6 vocum; Ich stuend an einem Morgen.

Other works:

> Lieder, sung or played (or both) on recorder, krummhorn, lute, etc.

Oberlinger positive organ.

Anthologies

BERUTTI, organ; CHORUS OF THE IMMACOLATA, BERGAMO,   ***62**
dir. CORBETTA. *The Organ "in cornu epistolae" of the Basilica of San Petronio, Bologna.*
Musical Heritage Society 1874 [1974].

Organ works:
> BRUMEL: Messa della Domenica.
> M.-A. CAVAZZONI: Ricercar.
> FOGLIANO: 3 ricercari.
> SEGNI: Ricercare per musica ficta in sol.

Vocal works by:
> ANONYMOUS, CARA, and TROMBONCINO.

Organ by Lorenzo di Giacomo da Prato, 1474-83.

BIGGS. *Historic Organs of Italy.*   ***63**
Columbia MS 7379.

> BANCHIERI: Dialogo.
> FANTINI: Corrente detta dello Staccoli.
> FRESCOBALDI: 3 Galliards; Capriccio sopra "La Battaglia."
> A. GABRIELI: Canzon ariosa.
> G. GABRIELI: Fuga del 9º tono.
> GESUALDO: Gagliarda del principe.
> MARCELLO: Psalm 19.
> B. PASQUINI: Variazioni sopra "La Folia."
> STORACE: Ballo della Battaglia.
> TRABACI: 2 Galliards.

ZIPOLI: 5 Versetti; Offertorio.

Five organs:
Antegnati (1635-36), San Carlo, Brescia; Callido (1797), Chiesa del Carmine, Ravenna; Serassi (1857), Chiesa Parochiale, Santa Anna di Borgo Palazzo, Bergamo; the two organs at San Petronio, Bologna — one by Lorenzo di Giacomo da Prato (1474-83), the other by Malamini (1596) with later revisions and additions.

BIGGS, organ; BOSTON BRASS ENSEMBLE, dir. BURGIN. *Music*   ***64**
for Organ and Brass.
Columbia MS 6117 (formerly issued as ML 5443).

Organ works:
FRESCOBALDI: Toccatas (d, G).
G. GABRIELI: Intonazione, Tones I-XII; Fantasia del 6⁰ tono.

Instrumental works (brass with organ and/or harpsichord) by FRESCOBALDI and G. GABRIELI.

DALLA LIBERA. *Antichi organi italiani: Lo storico organo di*   **65**
Pietro Nacchini (1751).
Vedette VST 6008. (Reissued by Christophorus, SCGLX 73830: *Sandro dalla Libera an der historischen Orgel des Konservatoriums zu Venedig* [1974].)

A. GABRIELI: Praeambulum quarti toni; Praeambulum tertii toni; Capriccio sopra il pass'e mezzo antico; Canzon ariosa; Ricercar arioso No. 1; Ricercar arioso No. 3; Ricercar del duodecimo tono; Toccata del decimo tono.
G. GABRIELI: Fantasia del sesto tono; Fantasia del quarto tono; Fuga del nono tono; Toccata; Ricercare No. 5; Canzon No. 2; Ricercar del decimo tono.

Nacchini organ (1751), Antico Conservatorio dell' Ospedaletto, Venice.

Review:
Organ Yearbook 8 (1977): 95.

EWERHART, organ; CONSORTIUM MUSICUM; RIAS   ***66**
KAMMERCHOR, dir. ARNDT. *Venedig: Festliche Kirchenmusik in San Marco.*
EMI 1C 037- 45 579.

Organ works:

> G. CAVAZZONI: Ave maris stella; Christe Redemptor omnium.
> A. GABRIELI: Ricercar II^i toni.
> G. GABRIELI: Intonazione.
> GUAMI: Canzon (a).

Vocal and instrumental works by:

> FANTINI, G. GABRIELI, and MONTEVERDI.

This seems to replace an earlier recording by the same performers on Odeon SMC (and STC) 91 117: *Musik in alten Städten und Residenzen: Venedig.*

HILDENBRAND. *Historische Orgeln in Brissago und*   **67**
Montecarasso. See **648**.

INNOCENTI, SPINELLI, TAGLIAVINI, and ZOJA.   ***68**
Europäische Orgellandschaften: Historische Orgeln in Italien.
Ariola Eurodisc XD 87 797 K. 2 LPs.

> ANTEGNATI: Antegnata.
> FRESCOBALDI: *Fiori musicali,* selections; Capriccio I (Bk. I); Toc-
> catas IV, X (Bk. II); Toccata X (Turin Ms.).
> A. GABRIELI: Canzon ariosa; Ricercar quinti toni.
> G. GABRIELI: Fuga del nono tono; Canzona I (1608).
> MERULA: Canzon IV; Sonata cromatica.
> MERULO: Toccata I.
> PADOVANO: Toccata del sesto tono.
> B. PASQUINI: Pastorale (G).
> PESCETTI: Sonata (c).
> ROSSI: Toccatas VI, XIV.
> D. SCARLATTI: Sonatas, K. 287, 288.
> TRABACI: Canto fermo II; Canzona francese; Durezze e ligature.
> ZIPOLI: Canzona V.

Four organs:

> Malamini (1596), San Petronio, Bologna; anonymous 17th c. organ,
> San Bernardino di Carpi, Modena; Callido (1791), Borca di Cadore;
> Serassi (1826), Cathedral of Brescia.

Reviews:

> *Ars organi* 26/55 (February 1978): 308; *Musik und Kirche* 47/1
> (January-February 1977): 34-35.

LITAIZE. *Les Sommets de l'orgue: Anciens Maîtres d'Espagne*   **69**
et d'Italie. See **823**.

PIERRE. *L'Orgue italien.* See **651**.   **70**

SAORGIN. *Orgues historiques,* vol. 8: *Santa Maria, Bastia.*   **71**
See **653**.

SAORGIN. *San Carlo Brescia.*   **72**
Harmonia Mundi 30.728.

> FRESCOBALDI: Aria detto balletto.
> A. GABRIELI: Ricercare arioso; Ricercare del 7º tono.
> G. GABRIELI: Canzon "La Spiritata."
> GUAMI: Toccata del 2º tono.
> MALVEZZI: Canzon del 2º tono.
> MERULA: Canzon "La Marca"; Toccata del 2º tono.
> B. PASQUINI: Introduzione e pastorale; Toccata VII.
> SODERINI: Canzon "La Scaramuccia."

Antegnati organ (1635-36), San Carlo, Brescia.

SCHUBA. *Master Organists of the 16th, 17th and 18th Centuries*   **73**
in Italy. See **654**.

SPINELLI. *The Organ "in cornu evangelii" of the Basilica of*   ***74**
San Petronio, Bologna.
Musical Heritage Society 3303 [1975].

> ANTEGNATI: Ricercare, Mode XI.
> G. CAVAZZONI: Pange lingua; Ave maris stella.
> A. GABRIELI: Toccata, Mode X; Canzon ariosa; Ricercare, Mode V.
> G. GABRIELI: Canzone "La Spiritata"; Intonazione and Fugue, Mode
>   IX; Toccata, Mode II.
> MERULO: Toccata prima, Mode XI.
> PADOVANO: Toccata, Mode VI.

PELLEGRINI: Canzone "La Serpentina."
VALENTE: Versi spirituali I, IV, V.

Malamini organ (1596), changed and enlarged in 1641, 1708, and 1812.

TERNI. *A Survey of the World's Greatest Organ Music: Italy,*   *75
vol. 1 — Composers from Emilia and Lombardy.*
Vox SVBX 5322. 3 LPs.

SIDE ONE.
  BANCHIERI: Sonata prima; Fuga plagale; Toccata prima del terzo
    tuono autentico alla elevatione del Santissimo Sacramento.
  G. CAVAZZONI: Canzon sopra "Il est bel et bon."
  M.-A. CAVAZZONI: Recercada.
  FOGLIANO: Recercare II and III; Recercada.
  SEGNI: Recercada.

SIDE TWO.
  BANCHIERI: Sonata sesta; Fuga triplicata; Sonata ottava in aria
    francese; Prima canzone italiana; Secondo dialogo, acuto e grave;
    La Battaglia; Ricercata del terzo et quarto tono.
  FATTORINI: Ricercare del terzo tono; Ricercare del nono tono.

SIDE THREE.
  ANONYMOUS: Sonata.
  G. C. ARRESTI: Sonata "Elevazione sopra il Pange lingua"; Sonata
    cromatica.
  LUZZASCHI: Toccata del quarto tono; Ricercare del secondo tono;
    Ricercare del primo tono.

SIDE FOUR.
  ALDOVRANDINI: Pastorale.
  BASSANI: Sonata.
  COLONNA: Sonata.
  SABADINI: Grave.

SIDE FIVE.
  F. ARRESTI: Elevazione; Ricercare.
  MARTINI: Preludio.
  MASCHERA: Canzone XXI.
  PELLEGRINI: Canzone "La capricciosa."

SIDE SIX.
  ANTEGNATI: Ricercare terzo, X tono; Ricercare I.
  MERULA: Sonata cromatica.
  SODERINI: Canzone "La ducalina."

Church of San Domenico di Prato, Florence (organ, 16th-19th centuries).

Review:

   Musik und Kirche 46/3 (May-June 1976): 142-43.

TERNI. *A Survey of the World's Greatest Organ Music: Italy,*   ***76**
vol. 2—*Lombard Composers and the Venetian School.*
Vox SVBX 5323. 3 LPs.

SIDE ONE.
   CAVACCIO: Canzon francese.
   A. CIMA: Canzone alla francese "La Novella."
   G. P. CIMA: Ricercare del V° tono.
   CORRADINI: Ricercare del IX° tono.

SIDE TWO.
   A. GABRIELI: Intonazione del I° tono; Intonazione del VII° tono;
      Ricercare del V° tono; Canzon ariosa; Ricercare del I° tono.

SIDE THREE.
   A. GABRIELI: Ricercare del XII° tono; Fantasia allegra; Ricercare del
      V° tono; Pass' e mezzo antico.

SIDE FOUR.
   PADOVANO: Ricercare del XII° tono; Toccata del VI° tono; Ricer-
      care del VI° tono.

SIDE FIVE.
   PARABOSCO: Ricercare; Mottetto-Ricercare "Da pacem Domine."
   BELL' HAVER: Toccata.
   SPERINDIO: Ricercare del III° tono; Ricercare del I° tono.

SIDE SIX.
   MERULO: Toccata I "Undecimo tono detto quinto"; Toccata del VII°
      tono.

Church of San Domenico di Prato, Florence (organ, 16th-19th centuries).

Review:

   Musik und Kirche 46/3 (May-June 1976): 142-43.

TERNI. *A Survey of the World's Greatest Organ Music: Italy,*   **77**
vol. 3—*Venetian School.* See **659**.

ZANABONI. *Antichi organi italiani: Storico organo construito*   **78**
da Antegnati nel 1581.
Vedette VST 6005.

> ANTEGNATI: Ricercare del X⁰ tono.
> G. CAVAZZONI: Kyrie, Christe, Kyrie (*Messa della Domenica*).
> M.-A. CAVAZZONI: Ave maris stella; Christe redemptor.
> FRESCOBALDI: Canzone IV (1627); Iste confessor; Toccata X (1614);
>   Toccata IV da sonarse alla levatione; Toccata V (Ms. Turino).
> A. GABRIELI: Canzone ariosa; Intonazione del VII⁰ tono.
> G. GABRIELI: Fuga del IX⁰ tono; "La Spiritata."

Antegnati organ (1581), San Giuseppe, Brescia.

ZANABONI. *Antichi organi italiani.*   **79**
Vedette VST 6009.

> ANONYMOUS (15th c.): Frottola; Canzone *a* 3.
> BANCHIERI: Dialogo acuto et grave; La Battaglia; Toccata I del ter-
>   zo tono.
> CIMA: Canzona alla francese "La Novella."
> FOGLIANO: 2 Recerchari.
> GABUZIO: Bicinium, "Surge amica mea."
> GASTOLDI: Bicinium, "Ad te, Domine, levavi."
> GUAMI: Canzon detta La Lucchesina.
> NANTERMI: Partita alla quarta bassa.
> PARABOSCO: Bicinium, "Benedictus."
> ROSSI: 2 Versetti.
> VALENTE: 2 Versi spirituali.

17th-century positive organ.

ZANABONI. *Antichi organi italiani.*   **80**
Vedette C2S 122 [1969].

> F. ARESTI: Elevazione; Ricercare.
> G. C. ARESTI: Suonata cromatica; Suonata elevazione sopra il Pange
>   lingua.
> BANCHIERI: Canzon ottava; Canzon undicesima; Kyrie, Christe,
>   Kyrie (*Messa della Domenica*); Suonata ottava in aria francese; Toc-
>   cata per l'elevazione.
> G. CAVAZZONI: Canzon sopra "Falt d'argens"; Iste confessor; Jesu
>   corona Virginum; Kyrie, Christe, Kyrie (*Missa Apostolorum*).
> M.-A. CAVAZZONI: Recercada del II⁰ tono; Salve virgo.

COLONNA: Sonata.
MARTINI: Elevazione II; Fuga; Sonata sui flauti, I & III.
MONARI: Sonate IX, X, XI.

Two organs, San Petronio, Bologna: Lorenzo di Giacomo da Prato (1475), and Baldassarre Malamini (1597).

Individual Composers

Cavazzoni, Girolamo

FARRELL, organ; ST. JOHN'S UNIVERSITY MEN'S CHOIR.   **81**
Organ Music of Girolamo Cavazzoni.
The Liturgical Press LPS 8146-0015.

> *Missa Dominicalis,* with choir and organ in alternation. Hymns: Exsultet caelum laudibus; Jesu corona virginum; Pange lingua; Veni Creator Spiritus. Canzona; Ricercare; Magnificat.

Holtkamp organ, St. John's University, Collegeville, Minnesota.

Gabrieli, Giovanni

BIGGS, organ; TARR BRASS ENSEMBLE; GREGG SMITH   ***82**
SINGERS. *The Glory of Venice: Gabrieli, Church Music.*
Columbia M-30937.

Organ works:
> Intonazione, Tones II, III, IV, and XI.

Works for choir and brass.

BIGGS, organ; GREGG SMITH SINGERS; TEXAS BOYS CHOIR   ***83**
OF FORT WORTH; TARR BRASS ENSEMBLE, dir. NEGRI. *The Glory of Gabrieli.*
Columbia MS 7071 and ML 6471 [1968].

Organ works:
> Intonazione, Tones I, VII-XI.

Works for multiple choirs, brass, and organ.

Rieger positive organ.

NOTE: In addition to **82** and **83**, Biggs has recorded a single work for solo organ (a ricercare) on Columbia MS 7142: *Gabrieli Canzonas for Brass, Wind, Strings and Organ.*

HEILLER, organ; CHOIR AND ORCHESTRA OF THE GABRIELI   **84**
FESTIVAL, dir. APPIA. *Processional and Ceremonial Music.*
Bach Guild HM 8 SD.

Organ works:
> Intonazione preceding the motets.

Other works:
> Motets, concerti, and the 15-part ricercar.

URBANCIC, organ; COLLEGIUM MUSICUM OF RADIO   ***85**
VIENNA, dir. KNEIKS. *Giovanni Gabrieli.*
Musical Heritage Society 998 [1969].

Organ works:
> Fugue, Mode IX; Toccata, Mode XI; Fantasia, Mode IV.

Instrumental canzonas for varying combinations.

CHAPTER 6
THE LOW COUNTRIES

Anthologies

PEETERS. *De Orgelkunst in de Nederlanden van de 16de tot de*   **86**
18de Eeuw. (The Organ and Its Music in the Netherlands 1500 to
1800.)
Musique Royale. 2 LPs. Records to accompany the book of the same title
by M. A. Vente and Flor Peeters (Antwerp: Mercatorfonds, 1971.)

> BULL: Fantasia on "Een kindekeyn is ons geboren"; Fantasia on "Laet
> ons mit herten reyne."
> CORNET: Fantasia, Mode VIII; Salve Regina.
> DE MACQUE: Canzona alla francese.
> FIOCCO: Andante (e).
> ISAAC: Herr Gott lass dich erbarmen.
> KERCKHOVEN: Prelude and Fugue (d); Verset, Mode VI "op den Cor-
> net"; Verset, Mode VII "op de Trompet"; Fantasia (F).
> PHILIPS: Fantasia (a); Trio du premier mode.
> SWEELINCK: Toccata (a); O Lux beata Trinitas; Echo Fantasy (a);
> Wo Gott der Herr nicht bei uns halt; Variations on "Est-ce Mars."
> VAN DEN GHEYN: Preludium (g).
> WILLAERT: Ricercar.

Four organs:
> Marekerk in Leiden (partially from the 16th c., later rebuilt);
> Bonifaciuskerk in Medemblik (Borstwerk from the 16th c., Hoofd-
> werk from the 17th, Rugwerk from the 18th c.); Nederlands Hervorm-
> de Kerk in Oosthuizen (16th c.); Sint-Maartenskerk in Haringe (18th
> c. Flemish).

TALSMA. *Die niederländische Orgelschule.*   **87**
Deutsche Grammophon (Archive) 198 445.

ANONYMOUS: Allemande; Branle champagne; Psaume 36; [untitled piece].

ATTAINGNANT: Tant que vivrai.

CLEMENS NON PAPA: Psaume 65 (*Souterliedekens*).

DE MACQUE: Durezze e ligature; Seconda stravaganze.

ISAAC: Herr Gott lass dich erbarmen.

KERCKHOVEN: Fantasia (C).

SERMISY: Tant que vivray.

STEENWICK: Serband.

SUSATO: Basse danse "Mon désir"; Ronde "Saltarello"; Ronde "Wo bist du."

SWEELINCK: Echo Fantasy (d); Fantasia; Malle sijmen; Toccata (G); Variations on "Von der Fortuna werd ich getrieben."

WILLAERT: Ricercar.

Four organs:

Noordwolde (Schnitger, 1695); Krewerd (anonymous builder, 1531); Medemblik (partially from the 16th c. with later additions in 1671, 1785, 1861); Oosthuizen (van Covelen, ca. 1530).

VERSCHRAEGEN. *L'Encyclopédie de l'orgue,* vol. 15: *L'Orgue*   **88** *des Flandres.* See **691**.

Individual Composers

Isaac, Heinrich

DERIEMAEKER. *Isaac: Orgelwerke.*   **89** Monumenta Belgicae Musicae MB 8.

Adieus mes amors; Benedictus; D. Brünle; Ein fröhlich wesen; Fortuna in mi; Frater Conradus; Graciensi plaisat; In meinem Sinn; La martinella; La morra; Nil n'est plaisir; Si dedero; Si dormiero; Tristitia vestra; Zwischen Berg und tiefem Tal.

Anthologies

BERNARD. *Berühmte Orgeln Europas: Altpolnische Orgelmusik.*   **90**
Electrola 1C 063-29 049.

> ANONYMOUS: Ferse/Tanze; Toccata; Cantilene/Dialog; Duo; Trio
> I; Trio II; Ferse; Trio III; Echo/La chasse; Introduktion; Tanz; Duo
> 1-3; Passepied; Fantasie; Fantasia (f); Interludium; Tanz; Fantasia;
> Fantasia cum canto fermo.

Organs:

> St. Johannis Church, Kasimierz (from 1620); Church of the Blessed
> Virgin Mary, Torún (from 1611); Monastery Church in Pelplin (18th
> century).

GRUBICH. *Polish Renaissance Organ Music.*   ***91**
Musical Heritage Society OR 339 (duplicates Muza SXL 235: *Musica antiqua Polonica*).

Works from the *Lublin Tablature,* the *Holy Ghost Monastery Tablature,* the *Pelplin Tablature,* and the *Warsaw Musical Society Tablature*:

> ANONYMOUS: (16th c.)—3 Praeambula; Colenda; Accede nuntia;
>> Tanz "Alla Poznanie"; Canzona; (17th c.)—Cantio polonica.
> CATO: Fantasia-Motet-Fuga.
> DE CRACOVIE: Praeambulum (F); Ave Jerarchia; Tanz Hayduczky.
> LEOPOLITA: Ricercare; Resurgente Christe Domino.
> PODBIELSKI: Praeambulum en sol.
> ROHACZEWHSKI: Canzona a quarto.
> ZELECHOWSKI: Fantasia.

Johannes Wolf organ (1763-93), Cathedral of Oliwa; rebuilt by Goebel (1934-36).

SCHOONBROODT. *Dance Music of the Renaissance from the*   ***92**
Tablature of Johannes von Lublin.
Musical Heritage Society 1323. (Duplicates Schwann VMS 2001.)

> 36 pieces from the *Lublin Tablature* (1540), including intabulations
> of works by Jannequin, Josquin, Willaert, and Nikolaj from Cracow.

Andries Severijn organ (1652), Onze Lieve Vrouw Basilica, Maastricht;
restored by Flentrop in 1963.

Review:
> *Organ Yearbook* 8 (1977): 94.

SEBESTYEN, harpsichord and organ. *La Renaissance en*   **93**
Pologne: Tablatures d'orgue et de luth.
Vox 30.021 (Candide).

> ANONYMOUS: Alius praeambulum (*Lublin Tablature*); Bransle de St.
>   Nicholas (*Fuhrmann's Lute Tablature*); Colenda; Dance Poznanie;
>   Dziwny Sposob; Ortus (*Holy Ghost Monastery Tablature*); 5 Polish
>   dances (*Gdansk Tablature*); Wesel.
> BAKFARK: 2 Fantasies.
> CATO: Fantasia and Fugue.
> DLUGURAJ: Cantio polonica; Fantasia; Villanella polonica; 4
>   Villanelles.
> LOHET: 3 Fugues (*Woltz Tablature*).
> MIKOLAJ Z KRAKOWA: Hayducky.
> POLAK: Gaillard (from Besard's *Novus partus*).
> WAISSELIUS: 2 Polish dances.

Anthologies

BEDOIS. *Portuguese Organ Music of the 16th and 17th*   **94**
Centuries. See **704**.

BERNARD. *Historic Organs of Europe,* vol. 1: *Sounds of*   **95**
XVIth-Century Spain.
Angel S 36914 (duplicates EMI 1C 063-29 050) [1972].

> BRUNA: Entrada por 2 órganos; Diálogo por trompetas.
> MORENO: Diálogo por trompetas; Diálogo.
> PALERO: Canción por flautas; Versillo; Canción; Trompetas.
> SEGOVIA: Diálogo; Danza; Canción; Duo; Canción; Elevación; Versillo; Entrada.
> SOTO: Entrade real; Interludi; Entrada por 2 órganos; Tiento por 2 órganos.
> TORRIJOS: Danza; Entrada; Canción con flautas.

Two organs in Aragon:
> Santa María, Daroca (partially from the 15th century, with 17th- and 18th-century additions); San Jaime, Calatayud (1550-90, by an anonymous builder).

BERNARD. *Old Spanish Organ Music.* See **706**.   **96**

BIGGS. *Organ Music of Spain and Portugal.*   ***97**
Columbia KL 5167 [1957].

AGOSTINHO DE CRUZ: Verso de 8º tono per do-sol-re.
CABANILLES: Tiento lleno por B cuadrado.
CABEZON: Dic nobis Maria.
CARREIRA: Fantasia.
CARVALHO: Allegro (D).
CASANOVAS: Paso en do.
JACINTO: Toccata.
B. PASQUINI. Partite sopra la aria della folia de Espagna.
SANTA MARIA: Fantasia primer tono.
SEIXAS: 5 Toccatas.
VALENTE: La Romanesca.

Organs:

Toledo Cathedral (Jose Verdalonga, 1801); University of Coimbra
(anonymous builder, 1733); Cathedral of El Pilar, Zaragoza (modern
instrument); Royal Palace, Madrid (Jorge Bosch, 1778); La Seo,
Zaragoza (Pedro Roques, 1860); Church of the Incarnation, Lisbon
(Antonius Xaverius, late 18th c.); National Monument of Mafra, Portugal (Joachim Antonio Peres Fontanes, 1807).

BILLETER, organ; RICERCAR-ENSEMBLE FÜR ALTE MUSIK   ***98**
(Zürich), dir. PIGUET. *Instrumental Variations in Spanish*
Renaissance Music.
EMI 1C 063- 30 116.

CABEZON: Ave maris stella VIII; Diferencias—Sobre conde claros;
Sobre el canto de la Dama le demanda; Sobre el canto llano de la
alta; Sobre la galliarda milanesa; D'où vient cela; Para quien crie
yo cabellos; Pavana italiana.
FLECHA: Ensaladas; Guerra; Justa.
NARVAEZ: Canción del Emperador; Diferencias sobre "Guardame
las vacas."
ORTIZ: Doulce mémoire; O felichi occhi miei; Passamezzo moder-
no; Recercadas II, IV.
TORRE: Cinco diferencias sobre "Las vacas."

CHAPELET. *Musique à la cour de Charles Quint; Musique à la*   ***99**
cour de Philippe II.
Harmonia Mundi HMU 705.

Contents are identical with those on the disc ("Trujillo") of the album *Orgues*
d'Espagne. See **102**.

CHAPELET. *The Organ of the Emperor in the Cathedral of*   ***100**
Toledo.
Musical Heritage Society 1216. (Duplicates Harmonia Mundi HMU
792, *Orgues d'Espagne: Toledo.*)

Contents are identical with those on the corresponding disc ("Toledo") of
the album *Orgues d'Espagne.* See **102.**

CHAPELET. *Orgues des Baléares,* vol. 1.   ***101**
Harmonia Mundi HMU 949.

> ANDREU: Tiento lleno a tres; Tiento partido de mano derecha a tres.
> BRUNA: Pange lingua.
> CABANILLES: Entrada de 4º tono; Tiento de falsas; Tiento XXIII
> por Alamire; Toccata de mano izquierda.
> LOPEZ: Dos versos para l'entrada de la Salve.
> VILA: Cinco versos de primer tono.

Caimari/Bosch organ (18th c.), Convent Sant-Geroni, Palma de Mallorca.

CHAPELET. *Orgues d'Espagne.*   ***102**
Harmonia Mundi 765. 5 LPs.

COVARRUBIAS.

> ARAUXO: Tiento de medio registro de tiple de 7º tono.
> BRUNA: Tiento sobre la letania de la Virgen; Tiento de falsas de 2º
> tono.
> CABANILLES: Corrente italiana.
> DURON: Gaitilla de mano izquierda.
> HEREDIA: Pange lingua a 3; Salve de lleno; Tiento de falsas de 4º
> tono; Tiento lleno del primer tono.
> MENALT: Tiento de falsas de 6º tono.
> SOLA: Medio registro de mano derecha.

Organ partially from the 15th or 16th century; enlarged ca. 1700 by Diego
de Orio Tejada.

PALMA DE MALLORCA.

> ANDREU: Tiento lleno a 3; Verso de 4º tono para despues de la
> Epistola; Tiento partido de mano derecha a 3.
> BERNABE: Tiento de falsas.
> BRUNA: Pange lingua; Tiento de dos tiples, 6º tono.

CABANILLES: Entrada de 4º tono; Tiento de falsas; Tiento XXIII; Pasacalle de primer tono; Toccata de mano izquierda.

LOPEZ: Dos versos para l'entrada de la Salve.

NASSARRE: Tiento a cuatro partido de mano derecha.

VILA: 5 Versos de primer tono.

18th-century Caimari/Bosch organ in the convent of Sant-Augusti.

SALAMANCA.

ALVARADO: Tiento por Delasolre.

ANONYMOUS: 4 Fauxbordons.

ARAUXO: Tiento de medio registro de baxón de 10º tono; Tiento de medio registro de tiple de 7º tono.

CABANILLES: Pasacalles de 4º tono; Tiento de falsas.

CABEZON: Tiento.

CASANOVAS: Pasos, Nos. 7 and 10.

LOPEZ: Versos de 4º tono; Versos de 7º tono.

MODENA: Tiento de 4º tono.

XIMENEZ: Batalla.

Salamanca Cathedral, organ by Pedro Liborno de Echevarría [1744], in a 16th-century case.

TOLEDO.

ANONYMOUS: Batalla famosa.

ARAUXO: Tiento de medio registro de baxón de 9º tono.

BERMUDO: Vexilla regis a 5; Cantus del primer tono; Conditor alme siderum.

CABEZON: 4 Versos del Kyrie del 4º tono.

CASANOVES: Paso V.

HEREDIA: Ensalada.

PERAZA: Medio registro alto del primer tono.

XIMENEZ: Batalla de 6º tono.

"Emperor's organ" at the Cathedral of Toledo, Renaissance case with pipework mainly from the 17th century.

TRUJILLO.

ANONYMOUS: Te matrem Dei; Jesucristo hombre y Dios; Sacris solemnis; Je vous. . . .

ARAUXO: Tiento de medio registro de baxón 6º tono.

A. CABEZON: O Lux beata Trinitas; 2 Tientos de primer tono; Tiento de 2º tono; Magnificat de primer tono; 4 versos de primer tono sobre "Saeculorum Amen"; Dic nobis Maria; Diferencias "Ave maris stella"; Tiento "Malheur me bat."

H. CABEZON: Dulce memoria.

D'ALBERTO: Tres.

GOMBERT: Fabordon Ileno; Fabordon glosado.
JANNEQUIN: Réveillez-vous.
JOSQUIN: Kyrie glosa por Palero.
SOTO DE LANGA: 2 Tientos.

18th-century organ.

CHAPELET. *Orgues d'Espagne.*   103
Harmonia Mundi 759.

ANONYMOUS: Je vous . . . ; Pour un plaisir; Réveillez-vous; Sacris
   solemnis; Versos arios; Batalla famosa (18th c.).
ARAUXO: Batalla de 6º tono; Tiento de medio registro de baxón de
   6º tono.
BERMUDO: Cantus del primero por mi bequadro; Conditor alme
   siderum.
BRUNA: Tiento sobre la letania de la Virgen.
CASANOVAS: Paso No. 7.
LOPEZ: 3 Versos de 4º tono.
MUDARRA: Gallarda.
PERAZA: Tiento de medio registro alto de 1º tono.

This recording seems to consist of selections taken from the 5-LP album of
the same name. See **102**.

CHAPELET. *Orgues espagnoles: Covarrubias.*   ***104**
Harmonia Mundi HM 793.

Contents are identical with those on the corresponding disc ("Covarrubias")
of the album *Orgues d'Espagne.* See **102**.

CHAPELET. *Orgues espagnoles: Covarrubias.*   105
Harmonia Mundi HMS 540 [1968].

ANONYMOUS (16th c.): 3 Fabordones.
ARAUXO: Tiento de medio registro de tiple de 10º tono; Tiento pe-
   queño y fácil de 7º tono; Tiento de medio registro de tiple de 7º
   tono; Tiento de 4º tono; Tiento de medio registro de 2 tiples de
   2º tono; Canto llano de la Immaculada Concepción.
CABEZON: Tiento de 1º tono; Diferencias sobre la gallarda milanesa;
   Tiento "Ut queant laxis"; Magnificat de 4º tono.
LOPEZ: 2 versos de medio registro; 4 Versos de 1º tono.

Organ partially from the 15th or 16th century; enlarged ca. 1700 by Diego
de Orio Tejada.

CHAPELET. *Orgues espagnoles: Salamanca.*   **106**
Harmonia Mundi HMS 541.

Contents are identical with those on the corresponding disc ("Salamanca")
of the album *Orgues d'Espagne.* See **102.**

CHAPELET. *Orgues historiques,* vol. 14: *Ciudad Rodrigo.*   **107**
Musique de Tous les Temps OH 14 [1966]. A 45-rpm record with
multi-page booklet (in French) on the organ.

> ARAUXO: Tiento de medio registro de baxón, 6º tono.
> CABEZON: Je vous . . . ; Gallarda; Magnificat, 7º tono.
> NARVAEZ: Canción del Imperador.
> SANTA MARIA: Fantasias, 7º & 8º tono.

Cathedral of Ciudad Rodrigo.

CHAPELET. *Orgues historiques,* vol. 7: *Covarrubias.*   **108**
Musique de Tous les Temps OH 7 [1964]. A 45-rpm record with
multi-page booklet (in French) on the organ.

> ANONYMOUS: 3 Fabordones.
> ARAUXO: Tiento de medio registro de 2 tiples de 2º tono.
> CABANILLES: Tiento de falsas.
> SEGNI DA MODENA: Tiento de 4º tono.

Organ discussed at **105.**

CHAPELET. *Orgues historiques,* vol. 10: *Salamanca.*   **109**
Musique de Tous les Temps OH 10 [1965]. A 45-rpm record with
multi-page booklet (in French) on the organ.

> CABEZON: Magnificat de 1º tono (2 versos). Improvisations by
> Chapelet.

Organ by Pedro Liborno de Echevarría (1744), in a 16th-century case.

CHAPELET. *Orgues historiques: Le Monde de l'orgue,* no. 10:   ***110**
Orgues de Castille, part 1. See **714.**

COCHEREAU and JONES. *Portugal's Golden Age,* vols. 4/5.   **111**
See **716.**

FROIDEBISE. *Hommage à Pierre Froidebise.*   **112**
Musique en Wallonie MWL 503 [1973]. (Duplicates a Ducretet-
Thomson release of 1957.)

> ANONYMOUS (16th c.): Faux-bourdons en dialogue.
> ARAUXO: Lauda Sion.
> BERMUDO: Cantus del primero por elamí; Cantus del primero por
> mi; Tantum ergo.
> CABEZON: Magnificat del 4º tono; Discante sobre la pavana italiana.
> PERAZA: Medio registro alto de 1º tono.
> SANTA MARIA: 8 Fantasias.

Historic organ restored by Flentrop (1955), Séminaire de Saint Trond.

FROIDEBISE, organ; ROGER BLANCHARD VOCAL ENSEMBLE.   ***113**
Music from the Chapel of Philip II of Spain.
Nonesuch 71016.

Organ works:

> CABEZON: D'où vient cela; Pavane; Diferencias sobre el canto del
> caballero.

Choral works by:

> MORALES and VICTORIA. Vocal works, with lute accompaniment,
> by MUDARRA.

Schnitger organ, Laurenskerk, Alkmaar.

LITAIZE. *Les Sommets de l'orgue: Anciens Maîtres d'Espagne et*   **114**
d'Italie. See **823.**

LLOVERA and TORRENT. *Hispaniae Musica,* vol. 4: *Orgel-*   **115**
werke des 16. Jahrhunderts.
Deutsche Grammophon (Archive) 198 455 [1969].

> BAZEA: Tiento de 7º tono.
> BERMUDO: Exemplo del modo primero por elamí.

CABEZON: Diferencias sobre "Guardame las vacas"; Tiento de 1º
tono; Tiento del 6º tono; Tres diferencias sobre el canto llano de
la alta; Diferencias sobre el canto del caballero.
D'ALBERTO: Salmo II "Qui habitat."
LACERNA: Tiento de 6º tono.
MORALES: Verso de 5º tono.
PALERO: Glosado del verso de Morales; Tiento "Cum Sancto Spiritu."
PERAZA: Tiento de medio registro alto de 1º tono.
SANTA MARIA: Fantasias III and IX.
SOTO: Tiento de 6º tono.

Three organs:

One in La Seo, Zaragoza, with 15th-century Gothic case and 18th-
century pipework; the "Emperor's organ" at Toledo, with casework
from 1543-49, but most of the pipework from the 17th century; and
an organ by Jose Bosca in the chapel of San Severo, Barcelona (1721).

LYMAN, organ; MONTREAL BACH CHOIR, dir. LITTLE;   **116**
CONSORT OF VIOLS, dir. JOACHIM. *Music of the Spanish
Renaissance.*
Turnabout TV 34264.

Organ works:

CABEZON: Dic nobis Maria; Duo; Versos de 1º, 4º y 5º tono.
ORTIZ: Recercada (organ with viol consort).
SANTA MARIA: Clausulas de 1º tono.
VALENTE: La romanesca con cinque mutanze.

Vocal or instrumental works by:

ALONSO, ANCHIETA, ANONYMOUS, ENSINA, ESCOBAR, FUEN-
LLANA, MILAN, and VICTORIA.

MERSIOVSKY. *Die Orgel in São Vicente de Fora, Lissabon.*   **117**
See **720**.

RILLING. *Spanish Organ Music.* See **721**.   **118**

TORRENT. *Portugaliae musica,* vol. 4: *Orgelwerke des 16.*   **119**
Jahrhunderts.
Deutsche Grammophon (Archive) 2 533 069 [1971].

CARREIRA: Canção a quatro glosada; Outro tento a quatro de 8º tom sobre un téma de canção; Primeira fantasia a quatro de 8º tom; Primeiro tento a quatro em sol; Tento a quatro de 2º tom; Tento a quatro em fa; Tento a quatro sobre o vilancico "Con qué la lavaré."

COELHO: Primeiro tento de 8º tom natural; Terceiro tento de 3º tom natural; Terceiro tento de 4º tom natural.

DE PAIVA: Tento de 4º tom; Tento no modo de mi, 3º tom.

Organ in the Cathedral of Evora, a Renaissance instrument (ca. 1562) rebuilt in the 18th century by Oldovini.

TORRENT, organ; BALCELLS, harp; BUSTAMENTE, soprano;   ***120**
SANTOS, harpsichord. *Musique à la cour de Charles Quint.*
Harmonia Mundi HM 10 001.

BERMUDO: Modo primero por mi y modo octavo por elamí.

CABEZON: Canción glosado "Ardenti mei suspiri"; Tiento de 4º tono; Tiento de 5º tono.

MUDARRA: Claros y frescos ríos; Gentil caballero.

NARVAEZ: Baja de contrapunto; Octavo tono; Canción del Emperador; 4 Diferencias sobre "Guardame las vacas"; Otras diferencias hechas por otra parte; 6 Diferencias sobre "O gloriosa Domina."

SANTA MARIA: 4 Fantasias.

SCHLICK: Salve regina.

Vocal and instrumental works by:

VALDERRABANO and VASQUEZ-FUENLLANA.

Individual Composers

Cabezón, Antonio de

CHAPELET.   **121**
Harmonia Mundi HM (25) OPUS 15.

Dic nobis María; Magnificat de 1º tono; Magnificat de 4º tono; Magnificat de 7º tono; O Lux beata Trinitas; 4 Versos sobre "Ave maris stella"; Tiento de 1º tono; "Malheur me bat"; 4 Versos de 1º tono sobre "Saeculorum Amen."

KANN, organ and clavichord; WITOSZYNSKI, vihuela. *Cabezón:*　***122**
Music for Organ, Clavichord and Vihuela de mano.
Musical Heritage Society 1223.

> 6 Tientos in various modes; Descant on the Italian Pavane; Kyrie
> Versets; "Ave maris stella" versets; Variations on "La Dama le deman-
> da"; Fabordones in the 5th mode.

MERSIOVSKY. *Antonio de Cabezón: Orgelwerke.*　　　　***123**
EMI 1C 065-99 678.

> Au joly bois sur la verdue; Fabordones del 1º tono; Tiento II de 4º
> tono; Discante sobre la pavana italiana; Diferencias sobre la Gallar-
> da milanesa; Ayme qui vouldra; Susanne un jour; Diferencias sobre
> el canto de la Dama le demanda; Versos del 7º tono; Tiento III de
> 1º tono; Magnificat Verses, 7º tono; Ultimi miei sospiri.

Pedro Librona de Echevarría organ (1755-57), Cathedral of Toledo.

ORTIZ. *History of Spanish Music,* vol. 8: *Organ Music of*　***124**
Cabezón.
Musical Heritage Society 436. (Duplicates Hispavox HHS3 and Erato STU
70 777.)

> Diferencias sobre el canto del caballero; Diferencias sobre la gallar-
> da milanesa; Discante sobre la pavana italiana; D'où vient cela; Fabor-
> dón de 4º tono; Tientos III de 1º tono, V de 2º tono, VII de 4º tono,
> VIII de 8º tono, XI de 5º tono, X de 1º tono.

Organs:

> Covarrubias (see **105**); Santa María, Daroca (see **95**).

Review:

> *Organ Yearbook* 6 (1975): 172.

Anthologies

BERNARD and HOGWOOD, organ; THE EARLY MUSIC CONSORT OF LONDON, dir. MUNROW. *Instruments of the Middle Ages and Renaissance.* See **1**. 125

BIGGS. *Historic Organs of Europe: Switzerland.* See **2**. 126

BOVET. *L'Orgue de Valère.*   *127
VDE-Gallo VG 3 088.

> ANONYMOUS: Felix namque; Upon la mi re; My Lady Careys Dompe; *Robertsbridge Codex* selections (Adesto, Estampie, Retrové, Tribum quem).
> BACH: Fantasy and Fugue (a), S. 561.
> G. GABRIELI: Canzon "La Spiritata."
> GUAMI: Canzona "La Lucchesina."
> TRABACI: Durezze e ligature.

Gothic organ (ca. 1380), rebuilt by M. Carlen (1718), with pedal added, Sion, Switzerland.

CHAPELET. *Musique à la cour de Charles Quint; Musique à la cour de Philippe II.* See **99**. 128

CHAPELET. *Orgue historique de Frederiksborg.*   ***129**
Harmonia Mundi HM 579.

> ANONYMOUS (English): La shy muse; My Lady Careys Dompe; La
> Dounce cela.
> CABEZON: Discante sobre la pavana italiana.
> B. PASQUINI: Variazioni sopra "La Folia."
> SCHEIDT: Toccata; Bergamasca; Variations on "Ei du feiner Reiter";
> Variations on a Galliard of John Dowland.
> SWEELINCK: Toccata; Variations on "Est-ce Mars"; Ricercare brevis;
> Variations on "Mein junges Leben hat ein End."
> VALENTE: La Romanesca.

Compenius organ (1612-16), Frederiksborg Castle, Hilleröd, Denmark.

CHAPELET, organ; ARS MUSICAE DE BARCELONA; ENSEMBLE ***130**
RICERCARE. *Un bal chez Rabelais.*
Harmonia Mundi 931.

> ANONYMOUS: La shy muse; My Lady Careys Dompe; La Dounce
> cela; Suites II, III, IV.
> FLEXTA: Branle "La Guerra."
> MILAN: Pavana III.

Compenius organ (see **129**).

CHAPELET and ROGG. *Danses de la Renaissance à l'orgue et*   ***131**
au clavecin.
Harmonia Mundi 2.465. 2 LPs.

> ANONYMOUS: La Dounce cela; La Shy myse; Muscadin; My Lady
> Careys Dompe; Why aske you.
> BULL: Galliarda; Galliarda to My Lord Lumsleys Pavan; Pavana.
> BYRD: Alman; Galinno custurame; Galliardas; John, come kiss me
> now; La Volta; Miserere; Passamezzo.
> CABEZON: Discante sobre la pavana italiana.
> FARNABY: Fantaysia; Pawles Wharfe; Quodlings Delight; Tower Hill;
> Up tails all.
> MUNDY: Robin.
> B. PASQUINI: Variazioni sopra "La Folia."
> SCHEIDT: Bergamasca; Toccata; Variations on a Dutch song; Varia-
> tions on a Galliard of John Dowland.
> SWEELINCK: Ricercar brevis; Toccata; Variations on "Est-ce Mars";
> Variations on "Mein junges Leben hat ein End."

TOMKINS: A Short Verse.
VALENTE: La Romanesca.

Instruments:

Chapelet—Compenius organ (1612-16), Frederiksborg Castle, Denmark; Rogg—a 16th-century table organ and a Ruckers/Taskin harpsichord.

CHAPUIS, DARASSE, HRON, et al. *Orgelmusik aus vier*   **132**
Jahrhunderten. See **759**.

COCHEREAU. *Les Maîtres d'orgue de Chartres.*   **133**
Philips 6504.026.

BRUMEL: Benedictus; Regina coeli; Sicut lilium inter spinas.
JULLIEN: Suite, 3ème ton; Fantaisie chromatique; Prelude à 5 parties; Tierce en taille.
TINCTORIS: Vostre regart.

DE KLERK. *Die Kleinorgel* (Historic Cabinet and Portable   ***134**
Organs).
Telefunken (Das alte Werk) 6.41 036.

BUXTEHUDE: Wie schön leuchtet der Morgenstern.
CASANOVES: Sonata V.
M. CORRETTE: Vous qui désirez sans fin.
L. COUPERIN: Chaconne (d).
FRESCOBALDI: Ave maris stella.
GIBBONS: A Fancy (a); The King's Juell.
PALESTRINA: Ricercare primi toni.
SANTA MARIA: Fantasias, Tones I, III, VIII.
SWEELINCK: Von der Fortuna werd' ich getrieben.
ZIPOLI: Canzona.

Organs:

A 16th-century regal; a 17th-century positive; a table organ of 1684; a secrétaire organ, ca. 1785; Schrein organ, early 18th century; 5 cabinet organs—ca. 1670, 1772, 1780, 1784, and 1790.

Review:

Musik und Kirche 50/1 (January-February 1980): 37-38.

EXTERMANN. *Swiss Historic Organs.* **135**
Jecklin 119.

Works of:
 BACH, BRUMEL, CABANILLES, GABRIELI, and PERGOLESI.
Two organs in the Wallis (Valois) canton: St. Georgs Pfarrkirche, Ernen;
St. Theodulskirche, Sion.

FROIDEBISE, P., organ; ROGER BLANCHARD VOCAL ***136**
ENSEMBLE. *Music from the Chapel of Charles V.*
Nonesuch H-71051 [1964].

Organ works:
 SCHLICK: Ascendo ad patrem; Gaude Dei genitrix; Maria zart.
Choral works of:
 CRECQUILLON and GOMBERT.
F. C. Schnitger organ, Laurenskerk, Alkmaar.

GWINNER, OEHMS, PIPER, and ROVATKAY. *Historische* **137**
Orgeln Niedersachsen. See **777.**

HASELBÖCK, F. *Ergetzlich Tanntzereyen.* ***138**
Da Camera 93 216.

 AMMERBACH: Herzog-Moritz-Tanz mit proportio.
 ANONYMOUS: 2 Corantos; Dalling Alman; Daunce; Nowel's Galliard
 (all from *Fitzwilliam Virginal Book*); Le Forze d'Hercole; Fusi
 Pavana piana; Passamezzo antico; Saltarello del re; Venetiana
 gagliarda.
 ATTAINGNANT: Basse danse; Branle gay; 2 Gaillardes; Pavane.
 BYRD: Alman; Coranto; A Gigg; La Volta.
 FACOLI: Aria della Signora Lucilla; Tedesco dita l'Austria; Tedesco
 dita la Proficia.
 JAN DE LUBLIN: Conradies; Hayduczky; Hispaniarum; Italica;
 Poznanie.
 KOTTER: Spaniol Kochersberg.
 NÖRMIGER: Intrada; Der mohren Auftzugh.
 PAIX: Schirazula marazula; Ungarescha und Saltarello.

SCHMID: Alemando novelle; Ein guter neuer Dantz; Der Hupfauf;
Le Corante de Roy; Ein schöner englischer Dantz; Der Hupfauf.
VALENTE: Lo ballo dell'intorcia.

HILDENBRAND. *Historische Orgeln aus der Schweiz.* See **792.**   **139**

HILDENBRAND. *Historische Orgeln in St. Gallen.* See **793.**   **140**

HOGWOOD, organ; EARLY MUSIC CONSORT OF LONDON,   ***141**
dir. MUNROW. *The Art of the Netherlands.*
Seraphim SIC-6104 [1976]. 3 LPs.

Organ works, which constitute a minority of the works in this set, are as
follows:
ANONYMOUS (16th c.): Adieu mes amors; Est-il conclu par un arrêt
d'amour (Basel University Library, Ms. F. IX. 22).
HOFHAIMER: Ein fröhlich Wesen.

Other works:
Secular songs, mass movements, motets, and instrumental music from
the period 1450-1550.

Organs:
Mander regal (Hofhaimer works); Mander positive (anonymous
works).

ISOIR, organ; GIBOUREAU, oboe. *Orgue et hautbois.*   ***142**
Studios S.M. T-445.

Works for organ alone:
ANONYMOUS (16th c.): La Dounce cela.
BALBASTRE: Au jô de pubelle; Que tu grô jan, quel folie.
GERVAISE: Branle.
LOEFFELHOLTZ: Intrada.
NEUSIEDLER: Judentanz.
PAIX: Ungarescha et Saltarello.
SCHMID: Alemande novelle et proportz; La Corante du roy; Ein
schöner englischer Tanz.

SUSATO: Ronde et Saltarelle.
SWEELINCK: Balletto del Granduca.

Works for organ and oboe:
KREBS: Fantaisie (f).
TELEMANN: 2 Sonatas (a, b).

JAQUET. *La Musique d'orgue en Europe du Moyen Age à la*   **143**
Renaissance. See **7**.

JAUD. *Historische Orgeln: Ebert-Orgel in der Hofkirche zu*   ***144**
Innsbruck.
Calig 30449.

BULL: In nomine.
BYRD: Ut re mi fa sol la.
HASSLER: Canzon; Wir glauben all' an einen Gott.
ISAAC: Ein frewlich Wesen; Gracieuse plaisante; Herr Gott, lass dich
erbarmen.
KOTTER: Praeludium in la.
SCHLICK: Maria zart.
SCHMID the ELDER: Ein guter neuer Dantz "Du hast mich wollen
nemmen."
SWEELINCK: Toccata (a); Echo Fantasia; Praeludium.
TALLIS: Remember not, O Lord.

Ebert organ (1558), restored by Ahrend, Court Church, Innsbruck.

Review:
Organ Yearbook 10 (1979): 176-77.

KRAPP. *Orgeln im Deutschen Museum: Edgar Krapp spielt auf*   ***145**
den Orgeln der Musikinstrumentensammlung.
Deutsches Museum, München 0666593 [1979].

ANONYMOUS: Voluntary I (*Six Voluntaries from Different Masters*).
BACH: Vom Himmel hoch, S. 701.
BEETHOVEN: Scherzo (G) (*Suite für mechanische Orgel*).
FROBERGER: Ricercare (e).
A. GABRIELI: Toccata 10º tono.
G. GABRIELI: Ricercare (a).

HANDEL: Allegro, Allegretto, and Gigue (*Pieces for a Musical Clock*).
HASSLER: Canzon (g).
HAYDN: Presto (*Flötenuhrstücke*, 1792).
PACHELBEL: Christus der ist mein Leben.
REGER: Weihnachten, op. 145/3.
SCHUBERT: Wohin soll ich mich wenden (*Deutsche Messe*).
SWEELINCK: Variations on "Mein junges Leben."

Historic instruments from the music instrument collection of the Deutsches Museum, Munich:

Church organ from 1630; Concert organ from 1923; six positive organs dated 1693, end of the 17th c., 2nd half of the 18th c., end of the 18th c., ca. 1800, 1809.

KRUMBACH. *Das Orgelportrait: Friesische Orgelpracht,* part 1. ***146**
Psallite PET 68 040 768.

ANONYMOUS: Frysicum.
BERFF: Mogt ick, o Swaentjen.
BROEKHUISEN: Mogt ick, o Swaentjen.
BRUMEL: Messa della Domenica.
BULL: Fantasia on a Fugue of Sweelinck.
ILEBORGH: Frowe al myn Hoffen an dyr Lyed.
KLEBER: Fantasia seu praeambulum.
KOTTER: Aus tiefer Not.
LUBLIN: De profundis.
PAUMANN: Mit ganczem Willen.
PAUMGARTNER: Praeambulum super f.
SCHEIDT: Pavana hispanica, variations 2, 3, 4, 6.
SWEELINCK: Pavana hispanica, variations 1, 5, 7, 8; Praeludium (F).
WECK: Spaniöler Tanz und Nachtanz.

Organs in Rysum and Osteel.

KRUMBACH and OPP. *Music for Two Organs.* ***147**
Musical Heritage Society 1217. (Duplicates Christophorus SCGLX 75901 and Oryx 1765.)

C. P. E. BACH: 4 Duets, Wq. 115; Allegro (Bb); Poco Adagio (F); Poco Adagio (a); Allegro (Eb).
BIUMI: Canzona (g).
CRECQUILLON: Cancion "Belle sans paire."
ROVIGO: Canzona (C).

STEIBELT: Sonata (G).
TOMKINS: A Fancy for Two to Play.
TROFEO: Canzona (g).

Joh. Chr. Köhler choir organs (1759-60), Ebrach Abbey. (Most of these works are not in their original form, but have been arranged for two organs.)

LEHRNDORFER. *Hoforganisten aus vier Jahrhunderten.*   ***148**
Musica Bavarica 801. (7" record.)

G. GABRIELI: Fugue, Tone VIII.
GUAMI: Canzon (a).
HOLZNER: Canzone (g).
KERLL: Aria con variazioni.
MICHL: Praeambulum (F).
MOSSMAYR: Andante grazioso.

A 3-stop table-top positive in the Munich *Residenz*. The instrument dates from ca. 1600 and is possibly the positive built in 1601 by Urban Häusler for Maximilian.

LEONHARDT. *Alpenländer.*   **149**
Philips 6775 006 [ca. 1973]. 2 LPs. (Also on Seon label ABCL-67008/2).

ANONYMOUS: Cathaccio; Gagliarda; Lodensana; Gagliarda; Pavan
  and Galliard.
AMMERBACH: Wer das Töchterlein haben will.
BLITHEMAN: Eterne rerum conditor.
EBERLIN: Toccata VI; Toccata et Fuga III.
FISCHER. Preludes and Fugues (b, D, E♭, c).
FROBERGER: Ricercar No. 1; Capriccio No. 8.
FUX: Sonata No. 5.
KERLL: Canzona (g); Toccata con durezze e ligature.
KREBS: Praeambulum sopra "Jesu meine Freude"; Jesus meine Zuver-
  sicht; Von Gott will ich nicht lassen.
MERULA: Un cromatico ovvero capriccio.
GEORG MUFFAT: Fuga (g).
NEWMAN: Pavan.
PACHELBEL: Alle Menschen müssen sterben; Magnificat Fugues Nos.
  4, 5, 10, 13; Toccata and Fugue (B♭).
B. PASQUINI: Canzone francese No. 7; Ricercare No. 4.
STORACE: Ballo della battaglia.

TAYLOR: Pavan and Galliard.
ZACHAU: Prelude and Fugue (G).

Organs in Austria, Italy, and Switzerland, as follows:
Choir organ (1757), Stiftskirche, Stams, Tyrol; choir organ (1746),
Stiftskirche, Wilhering, near Linz; choir organ (ca. 1650), Stiftskirche, Wilten, Innsbruck; organ in Churburg Castle, Val Venosta; 18th-
century organ, St. Jakobus-Kirche, Compatsch, Graubunden; Gospel
organ (1743-44), Klosterkirche, Muri, Aargau.

LITAIZE. *Les Sommets de l'orgue: Anciens Maîtres d'Espagne*   **150**
et d'Italie. See **823**.

LUY.   **151**
Gallo VG 3 002.

ANONYMOUS: Whose faithful service.
BACH: Chorales, S. 659, 665, 667; Prelude and Fugue (D), S. 532.
CABEZON: Diferencias sobre el canto del caballero.
FRESCOBALDI: Capriccio No. 3 (1624?).
G. GABRIELI: La Spiritata.
GRIGNY: Dialogue sur les grands jeux.
VAN NOORDT: Psalm 24.

METZGER, RIEDL, WALTER, and WALTERSKIRCHEN,   ***152**
claviorganum; SIMA, soprano; STURM, alto; SALAMONSBERGER,
tenor; HAHN, bass; GUTTMANN, lute. *Claviorganum Musik in der Salz-
burger Residenz.*
EMI 065- 99 818.

Claviorganum works:
BYRD: Fantasia No. 4.
CABANILLES: Tiento No. 2.
CHAMBONNIERES: Double; Jeunes Zephirs.
ERBACH: Canzon, Tone IX.
HOFHAIMER: Carmen Magistri Pauli.
KLEBER: Fantasia in fa.
LUBLIN TABLATURE: Selections.
PAIX: Ungarescha.
POGLIETTI: Über das Hennergeschrey.

SCHMID: Alemande novelle.
STORACE: Ballo della battaglia

Instrumental and vocal works:
ANONYMOUS, MUDARRA, SENFL.

MICHEL. *Die historische Orgel der Klosterkirche Oelinghausen.*   **153**
See **828**.

MUSCH. *Music for Christmas.* See **828**.   **154**

MUSICA RESERVATA OF LONDON. *The Instruments of the*   **155**
Middle Ages and Renaissance. See **8**.

PEETERS. *De Orgelkunst in de Nederlanden van de 16de tot de*   **156**
18de Eeuw. See **86**.

ROGG, organ; ENSEMBLE RICERCARE; CLEMENCIC CON-   ***157**
SORT, dir. CLEMENCIC. *Danses du Moyen-Age.* See **10**.

ROGG. *Danses, Enigmes, Estampies.* See **11**.   **158**

ROGG, organ; CANZONA ENSEMBLE; CLEMENCIC CONSORT;   ***159**
ENSEMBLE RICERCARE; JAYE CONSORT OF VIOLS; ACCADEMIA
MONTEVERDIANA. *Dictionnaire des danses de la Renaissance.*
Harmonia Mundi HM 446. 3LPs.

Organ works, which constitute a minority of the contents of this record, are
as follows:
ASTON; Hornepype.
ATTAINGNANT: Cortesana padoana; Gaillarde.

> BENDUSI: Bassa imperiale.
> BUCHNER: Ach hülf mich Leid.
> SCHMID: Wie schön blüht uns der Maie.

Positive organ.

ROGG, positive organ; ENSEMBLE D'INSTRUMENTS ANCIENS   **160**
DE ZURICH. *Estampies, Basses danses, Pavanes.* See **12.**

SYNTAGMA MUSICUM OF AMSTERDAM, dir. OTTEN. *The*   **161**
Seraphim Guide to Renaissance Music.
Seraphim SIC 6052 [1969]. 3 LPs.

This set contains 72 vocal and instrumental pieces from the 13th to the 17th century. For organ, it illustrates the use of the portative with other instruments. Some of the works employing the portative are as follows:

> ANONYMOUS (14th c.): Di Molen van Paris (portative and fiddle);
>   Kyrie, *Faenza Codex* (recorder, portative, and fiddle).
> DES PREZ: La Bernardina (2 recorders and portative).
> GULIELMUS: La Bassa castiglia (recorder and portative).

Three solo keyboard works, recorded here on clavichord or spinet, are included as follows:

> LEGRANT: Piece from the *Buxheimer Orgelbuch.*
> PAUMANN: Untitled piece from the *Fundamentum organisandi.*
> SWEELINCK: Toccata.

Other selections are performed by various vocal and instrumental ensembles.

Awarded the *Grand Prix internationale du disque.*

TACHEZI. *Orgelmusik der Renaissance.*   ***161.1**
Telefunken 6.42 587.

> CABEZON: Diferencias sobre el Canto del Caballero.
> ERBACH: Ricercar im 2. Ton.
> HOFHAIMER: Recordare II.
> KOTTER: Salve Regina.
> MERULO: Toccata I.
> MILAN: Pavane.
> PELLEGRINI: La Serpentina.

M. PRAETORIUS: O lux beata Trinitas.
SANTA MARIA: Fantasia in 1. Ton.
VALDERRABANO: Fantasia primero grado.
Ebert organ, Hofkirche, Innsbruck.

TALSMA: *Die niederländische Orgelschule.* See **87.**   **162**

PART THREE

Baroque

CHAPTER 10
BOHEMIA AND MORAVIA

*An asterisk to the left
of an entry number indicates
that the recording was advertised
for purchase
as recently as 1978.*

Anthologies

HRON, KRAJS, NOVAK, ROPEK, and VACHULKA. *Orgeln*   ***163**
aus dem goldenen Prag.
Schwann AMS 2596.

> BRIXI: Toccata (D); Fugue (D).
> CERNOHORSKY: Fugues (c, g).
> LINEK: Pastorella.
> OTRADOVIC: Wedding March.
> SEGER: Preludes (c, A); Fugues (f, a).
> VANHAL: Fugue (C).
> ZACH: Prelude and Fugue (A).
> ZVONAR: Introduction and Fugue (c).

Organs in various Prague churches including: Naundt organ (1670-73), Týn church; Schwartz organ (1745-46), Sv. Mikuláš.

Review:
Organ Yearbook 8 (1977): 94.

RABAS, REINBERGER, and VODRAZKA. *Czech Organ Music*   ***164**
of the 18th Century.
Panton 110 418/19. 2 LPs.

> ANONYMOUS: Fugue (D); Fugue (e); Fugue (e) from the *Organ Book of F. Hulkas*; Fugue (C) from the *Organ Book of J. Slavik*; Fugue (D) on a Theme by F. X. Brixi; Fugue (D) on a Theme with Continuo Bass by F. X. Brixi; Fugues (e, A, a, d, f); Fugue (c) for Two Organs.
> KUCHAR: Fantasia (d).

REJCHA: Fugue (A).
SEGER: Fugue (f); Präludium (a).
VANHAL: Fugues, Nos. 1-6.
ZACH: Fugue (a).
ZIMMERMAN: Fugue (e).

Two Anton Gartner organs (1756 and 1766), monastery at Teplá.

Review:

Musik und Kirche 47/4 (July-August 1977): 189.

WALTER. *Böhmische Orgelmeister.*   *165
Christophorus SCGLX 73884.

CERNOHORSKY: Fugue (a).
EBEN: Moto ostinato aus der *Musica dominicalis.*
JANACEK: Postludium aus der *Glagolitischen Messe.*
KUCHAR: Fantasia (g).
LINEK: Fünf Intraden zur Krönung Maria Theresias 1743 (transcriptions of brass pieces).
MUSIL: Sonata solemnis.
SEGER: Christkindl-Pastorella e Motetto.
ZACH: Preludio e Fuga (g).

Gerhard Schmidt organ, Basilica of Altötting.

Review:

Musik und Kirche 50/1 (January-February 1980): 37.

Anthologies

BIGGS. *Historic Organs of England*. See **14**.   **166**

DANBY. *English Organs: St. Mary's Rotherhithe*.   ***167**
Oryx 511 and Exp 22. (Duplicated by Harmonia Mundi 729.)

> BLOW: Verse for Cornet and Single Organ.
> BOYCE: Voluntary (D).
> BULL: In nomine (No. 9).
> GIBBONS: Fancy for a Double Organ.
> PURCELL: Voluntary (G).
> TOMKINS: Short Verse; Voluntary (C).
> WALOND: Voluntaries (d, G).
> S. WESLEY: Air and Gavotte.

John Byfield organ (1764), restored by Mander (1959).

DARLING. *A Concert of Eighteenth-Century Music*.   ***168**
Colonial Williamsburg Foundation WS 105 [1974].

> ANONYMOUS: Fy gar rub her o'er with straw (variations); George
>   Washington's March.
> BLOW: Theatre Tune.
> CLARKE: King William's March; The Duke of Gloucester's March;
>   The Prince of Denmark's March; Trumpet Tune.
> HANDEL: Voluntary (C).
> LARINI: Lesson.

PURCELL: Old Hundredth.
SELBY: Voluntary (A).
WALOND: Voluntary (d).

Positive organ (ca. 1760) possibly by Snetzler, restored by Mander, and presently in the Sir Christopher Wren building of the College of William and Mary.

Reviews:

Organ Yearbook 6 (1975): 172-73; *Music/The AGO and RCCO Magazine* 9/1 (January 1975): 24-25.

DART, organ, harpsichord, clavichord. *Masters of Early English*   **169**
Keyboard Music. See **16**.

GIFFORD. *East Anglian Keyboard Music.*   ***170**
CRD 1057.

AMNER: 3 Verses on "O Lord in Thee."
BOYCE: Voluntary I.
BURNEY: Cornet Voluntary.
HOOK: Voluntary (c).
JONES: Church Piece IX.
QUARLES: A Lesson.
WHYTE: In nomine.

Thamar organ, St. Michael's Church, Framlingham (See **173**).

GIFFORD. *Organ Recital: Hexham Abbey.*   ***171**
Crescent ARD 116.

ARNE: Concerto I (excerpts).
BLOW: Voluntary for Double Organ.
GREEN: Voluntary VIII.
STANLEY: Voluntary VIII.
TOMKINS: Fancy; Voluntary.
Plus pieces by S. S. WESLEY, DAQUIN, and BACH.

JACKSON, N. *The Organ at Adlington Hall.*   ***172**
Musical Heritage Society 3335 [1976]. (Duplicates Oryx 1750.)

ANONYMOUS (*Robertsbridge Codex,* ca. 1350): Estampie.

> ANONYMOUS (ca. 1500): La mi re.
> BULL: Salve Regina; Carol "A child is born."
> CLARKE: Trumpet Tune (D); King of Denmark's March.
> CROFT: Trumpet Tune (D).
> PURCELL: Voluntary (G); Voluntary on "Old Hundredth."
> WALOND: Cornet Voluntary.

Bernard Smith organ (ca. 1670), Adlington Hall.

LANDALE. *L'Encyclopédie de l'orgue,* vol. 41: *L'Orgue anglais*   **173**
des XVIe, XVIIe et XVIIIe siècles.
Erato EDO 241.

> ARNE: Allegro con spirito.
> BENNETT: Voluntary (F).
> BLOW (attributed): Voluntary (d) for Double Organ.
> BOYCE: Voluntary (D).
> BULL: Noel "Een Kindekeyn is uns geboren."
> GIBBONS: Fantasia.
> LOCKE: Voluntary (A).
> PURCELL: Voluntary (G); Voluntary for a Double Organ.
> STANLEY: Voluntary (d).
> TALLIS: Iste confessor; Iam lucis orto sidere.
> THORLEY: Allegro for Flute Stop.
> TRAVERS: Cornet Voluntary.

Thamar organ, St. Michael's, Framlingham, with a case dating from ca. 1580, some pipework from 1674.

Review:
> *Organ Yearbook* 6 (1975): 171-72.

MARDIROSIAN. *English Cathedral Voluntaries of the 18th*   ***174**
Century.
Musical Heritage Society 1854.

> BENNET: Trumpet Voluntary.
> BOYCE: Voluntary (a).
> GOODWIN: Trumpet Voluntary.
> GREENE: Voluntary (C).
> ROSEINGRAVE: Voluntary (g).
> STANLEY: Voluntary (e).
> TRAVERS: Voluntary (C).
> WALOND: Cornet Voluntaries (d, e, G).

Reuter organ, Reformation Church, Washington, D. C.

MOE. *A Procession of Voluntaries.*   ***175**
Cambridge CRS 2540.

> ALCOCK: Voluntary (D).
> BOYCE: Voluntaries 1 (D), 4 (g).
> GREENE: Voluntaries 1 (G), 4 (g), 8 (c).
> STANLEY: Voluntaries Op. 5, No. 5 (D), Op. 7, No. 8 (a).
> WALOND: Voluntary Op.1, No. 6 (d).

Byfield organ (1764), restored by Mander (1959), St. Mary's Church, Rotherhithe, London.

MUSCH. *Englische Orgelmusik des 18. Jahrhunderts.*   ***176**
Christophorus SCGLX 73 865. (Reissued as Musical Heritage Society 4382.)

> BOYCE: Voluntaries 1 (D), 2 (G).
> GREENE: Voluntary 1.
> HANDEL: Voluntaries 1 and 5.
> STANLEY: Voluntary Op. 7, No. 6.
> WALOND: Voluntaries 3 and 6.
> S. WESLEY: *Twelve Short Pieces:* Nos. 5, 6, 8, 9, 11, 12, 13.

Riepp organs, Basilica of Ottobeuren.

Individual Composers

Boyce, William

WILLS. *Ely Cathedral Choir and Organ.*   ***177**
Saga 5440.

Organ:

> Voluntaries 1, 2, 4, and 10.

Choral music:

> 4 anthems.

Harrison organ (1908) in a Gilbert Scott case (1851).

Handel, George Frideric
Complete Concertos

ALAIN, organ; ORCHESTRE DE CHAMBRE PAILLARD, dir.   ***178**
PAILLARD. *16 Concertos pour orgue et orchestre.*

Erato STU 71097 [1977]. 4 LPs.

> Schwenkedel organ (1970), Collégiale de Saint-Donat.

Review:

> *Musik und Kirche* 48/4 (July-August 1978): 198-99.

This recording supersedes the same performers' recording on Erato STU 70074/5/6/7 [1961]. Available also on Erato label:

> Concertos 1-8 (DUE 20224, 2 LPs); Concertos 9-16 (DUE 20226, 2 LPs).

BIGGS, organ; LONDON PHILHARMONIC ORCHESTRA, dir.   ***179**
BOULT. *Organ Concertos Nos. 1-16.*
Columbia D3M 33716 [1975]. 3 LPs.

> The "Handel organ," St. James Parish Church, Great Packington. This is a reissue of D3S 777/78 [1968]. Note that the earlier recording also included the "Six Little Fugues," which are missing on D3M 33716.

CHORZEMPA, organ; CONCERTO AMSTERDAM, dir.   ***180**
SCHROEDER. *Organ Concertos Nos. 1-16.*
Philips 6709.009. 5 LPs.

> Dutch chamber organ (attributed to J. P. Künckel, ca. 1780) presently in the Old Catholic Parish Church of St. Anne and St. Mary, Haarlem.

Review:

> *The Organ* 55/219 (January 1977): 146-47.

EWERHART, organ; COLLEGIUM AUREUM, dir. PETERS.   ***181**
Organ Concertos Nos. 1-16.
Musical Heritage Society 305-308 [1971]. (Duplicates Oryx 305-308 and Harmonia Mundi 1C 197 99880/83.) 4 LPs.

Organs:

> Gabler (1737-50), Weingarten; Riepp (1757-66), Ottobeuren; Strumpfler cabinet organ (ca. 1760), Geertekerk, Utrecht; anonymous instrument (ca. 1770), Körbecke.

MALCOLM, organ; ACADEMY OF ST. MARTIN-IN-THE-FIELDS,   ***182**
dir. MARRINER. *Organ Concertos Nos. 1-16.*
Argo D 301/04. (Duplicates Telefunken 6.35 343.) 4 LPs

Byfield organ (1764), St Mary's Rotherhithe; Walker organ, Merton College, Oxford; organ at St. John the Evangelist, Islington.

Review:

The Organ 55/219 (January 1977): 146-47.

MÜLLER, organ; SCHOLA CANTORUM BASILIENSIS, dir. ***183**
WENZIGER. *Organ Concertos.*
Deutsche Grammophon (Archive) 2723.042. (A reissue of DG [Archive] 104 917/921 [1958].) 5 LPs.

Walcker positive organ.

PRESTON, organ; MENUHIN FESTIVAL ORCHESTRA, dir. ***184**
MENUHIN. *16 Organ Concertos.*
His Master's Voice SLS 824. 4 LPs.

Mander organ (1966), containing some Renatus Harris pipework, in Merchant Taylors' Hall, London; Flentrop organ (1966), Queen Elizabeth Hall, London; the "Handel organ" at St. James Parish Church, Great Packington.

Available also on EMI label:

Concertos 4, 6, 8, 10 (1C 037 00080); Concertos 1, 5, 13, 14 (1C 037 00096); Concertos 2, 3, 9, 15 (1C 037 02005); Concertos 7, 11, 12 (1C 037 02117).

ROGG, organ; ORCHESTRE DE CHAMBRE TOULOUSE, dir. ***185**
ARMAND. *Organ Concertos Nos. 1-16.*
Voix de Son Maître C 165-14.051/54. 4 LPs.

Abbey church of St-Michel, Gaillac:

Organ dates partially from 1684 and 1755/rebuilt by Dominique Cavaillé-Coll (1824) and by Daublaine et Callinet (1843).

TACHEZI, organ; CONCENTUS MUSICUS, VIENNA, dir. ***186**
HARNONCOURT. *Organ Concertos Nos. 1-16.*
Telefunken 6.35 282. 3 LPs.

Handel, George Frideric
Selected Concertos and/or Other Works

BIGGS, organ; LONDON PHILHARMONIC ORCHESTRA, dir.   ***187**
BOULT. *Four Favorite Organ Concertos.*
Columbia MS-6439.

> Op. 4, Nos. 2, 5; Nos. 13, 16.

DALLMANN, organ; HEIDELBERG KAMMERORCHESTER.   ***188**
Handel: Favourite Organ Concertos.
Oryx EXP 33.

> Op. 4, Nos. 1, 4; No. 13.

DE KLERK, organ; AMSTERDAM KAMMERORCHESTER, dir.   ***189**
RIEU.
Bärenreiter Musicaphon 1217.

> Op. 4, No. 5 (F); Op. 7, No. 3 (Bb); No. 13 (F) "Cuckoo and the
> Nightingale."

DE KLERK, organ; AMSTERDAM KAMMERORCHESTER, dir.   ***190**
VAN DER HORST. *Handel: Orgel- und Orchesterkonzerte.*
Telefunken 6.41 320; 6.41 327; 6.41 348. 3 LPs.

6.41 320.
> Organ Concertos 4, 8; Concerto grosso, Op. 6, No. 6.

6.41 327.
> Organ Concertos 14-16.

6.41 348.
> Organ Concertos 5, 9, 13.

GEHRING, W., organ; RHEINISCHES KAMMERORCHESTER   ***191**
KÖLN, dir. KOCSIS.
Christophorus SCGLX 73 786.

> Organ Concertos 4, 10, 13.

JACKSON, N., organ and harpsichord; BARKER, harpsichord.   ***192**
Oryx 1718.

Organ:

> Cornet Voluntary (g); Fantasia (C); Two Fugues (c, a); Voluntary (C).

Harpsichord:

> Suite (e); Suite (C) for two harpsichords; "Pigeon's Air."

Bernard Smith organ (ca. 1670), Adlington Hall.

JONES, G., organ; PHILHARMONIA ORCHESTRA, dir.   **193**
SCHÜCHTER.
EMI 1C 047-50511.

> Concertos 2, 4, 8.

KÖHLER, organ; GEWANDHAUS ORCHESTER, dir. THOMAS.   ***194**
Philips 6530 003; 6530 032. 2 LPs.

> Concertos Op. 4, Nos. 1-6.

LEHOTKA, organ; FRANZ LISZT CHAMBER ORCHESTRA, dir.   ***195**
SANDOR.
Hungaraton SLPX 11.380.

> Organ Concertos 1, 4, 5, 9.

MÜLLER, organ; SCHOLA CANTORUM BASILIENSIS, dir.   ***196**
WENZIGER.
Deutsche Grammophon has the following recordings of selected concertos:

DG 198 393.

> Concertos 4, 8, 11, 13.

DG 198 410.

> Concertos 1, 2, 3, 6.

DG 2535 264.

> Concertos 7, 9, 10, 13.

NÜTZEL, organ; MUNICH BACH CONSORT, dir. NÜTZEL.   ***197**
Musical Heritage Society 3597.

   Organ Concertos Op. 4, Nos. 1-4.

PRESTON, organ; MENUHIN FESTIVAL ORCHESTRA, dir.   ***198**
MENUHIN. *Organ Concertos.*
Angel S-36599 and S-36700. 2 LPs.

This is a re-issue of selected concertos drawn from His Master's Voice SLS
824. See **184**.

RICHTER, organ; KAMMERORCHESTER MÜNCHEN, dir.   ***199**
RICHTER.
Telefunken 6.41 565/6/7. 3 LPs.

   Concertos 1-12 (Op. 4 and Op. 7).

Locke, Matthew

TILNEY, organ and harpsichord. *Colin Tilney Plays the*   **200**
Keyboard Music of Matthew Locke.
Pye (Golden Guinea Collector Series) GLGC 14128 [1970].

Organ works:
   Voluntaries I-VII (*Melothesia*).
   Harpsichord suites and dances.
Byfield organ (1764), restored by Mander (1959), St. Mary's, Rotherhithe.

Purcell, Henry

BROSSE. *Oeuvres pour orgue.*   ***201**
Voix de Son Maître C 167-14 183. (Also on EMI 1C 065-14 183.)

   4 Trumpet Tunes; The Queen's Dolour; Prelude in G; 2 Almonds;
   3 Voluntaries
Organ at the Cathedral Sainte-Marie de Saint-Bertrand de Comminges.

Anthologies

ALAIN. *French Christmas Carols.*   ***202**
Musical Heritage Society 673. (Duplicates Erato STU 70.563 [1963].)

> DANDRIEU: 5 Noëls.
> DAQUIN: Noëls 1, 9, 10, 11.

Clicquot/Haerpfer-Ermann organ, Cathedral of Sarlat, Dordogne.

ALAIN. *Great Pages from French Organ Music.*   ***203**
Musical Heritage Society 758. (Duplicates Erato STE 50236: *L'Orgue français* [1964].)

> FREINSBERG (GUILAIN): Suite, 2ème ton.
> LEBEGUE: Suite, 2ème ton.
> MARCHAND: Dialogue (*Troisième Livre d'orgue*); Tierce en taille;
>   Basse de trompette.
> NIVERS: Suite du premier ton (*Troisième Livre d'orgue*).

Clicquot/Haerpfer-Ermann organ, Cathedral of Sarlat, Dordogne.

ALAIN. *Sacred Music in the Royal Chapel at Versailles.*   ***204**
Musical Heritage Society 931. (Duplicates Erato STU 70315: *Musique à Versailles* [1965].)

> MARCHAND: Tierce en taille; Dialogue.
> NIVERS: Suite, 2ème ton (*Troisième Livre d'orgue*).

Gonzalez organ, Palace of Versailles.

*205

ALAIN.
Musical Heritage Society 1022. (Duplicates Erato EDO 201: *L'Encyclopédie de l'orgue,* vol. 1: *L'Orgue français* [1967].)

> J. F. DANDRIEU: Excerpts from *1er Livre d'orgue:* Offertoire "O filii"; Basse de cromorne and Magnificat (Suite I); Flûtes, verset 5; Basse de trompette, verset 4; Magnificat (Suite IV); Offertoire and Trio (Suite V); Musette, Tierce en taille, and Offertoire (Suite VI).
> DUMAGE: *Livre d'orgue.*

Organ of anonymous origins, rebuilt by Callinet/restored by Kern, Cathedral of Uzès.

*206

ALAIN.
Musical Heritage Society 986. (Duplicates Erato EDO 202: *L'Encyclopédie de l'orgue,* vol. 2: *L'Orgue français* [1967].)

> CLERAMBAULT: *Premier Livre d'orgue:* Suites, 1er et 2ème tons.
> D'AGINCOUR: Suites, 2ème et 5ème tons.

Organ of anonymous origins, rebuilt by Callinet/restored by Kern, Cathedral of Uzès.

*207

ANTONINI, CHAPELET, and CHAPUIS. *Orgues de Provence.*
Harmonia Mundi HM 760.

> ANONYMOUS (16th/17th c.): Danses.
> ATTAINGNANT: Kyrie Cunctipotens (4 versets).
> F. COUPERIN: Gloria (*Messe des paroisses*).
> L. COUPERIN: Branle de Basque.
> FRESCOBALDI: Toccata per l'elevazione; Toccata settima; Canzone dopo l'elevazione.
> ROBERDAY: Fugues II, V, X, and XII.

Jullien organ (1690), Roquemare; Isnard organ (1772), Saint-Maximin; Piantanida organ (1820), Notre-Dame-des-Doms, Avignon; Piantanida organ, Manosque; Royer (1648)/Mentasti (1827) organ at L'Isle-sur-la-Sorgue.

*208

BAKER.
FY 043.

> CLERAMBAULT: Suites I and II.
> DUMAGE: *Livre d'orgue.*

BERNARD. *Altfranzösische Orgelmusik.* ***209**
EMI 1C 063-28 967 [1974].

> ANONYMOUS: Dialogue; Fugue/Final; 8 Bergerettes.
> GUILAIN: Suite, 2ème ton.
> RAISON: Mass, 1er ton.

Joyeuse/Gonzalez organ, Cathedral of Auch.

Review:

> *Musik und Kirche* 45/6 (November-December 1975): 309.

BETOULIERES. *Orgues historiques. Le Monde de l'orgue No. 2:* ***210**
Saint-Guilhem le Désert.
Harmonia Mundi HM 1.202.

> L. COUPERIN: Allemande; Fantaisie (C, No. 63); Chaconne (d); Duo;
> Passacaille; Fantaisie du 4e ton.
> ROBERDAY: Fugues et Caprices Nos. 1, 2, 3; Fugues Nos. 11 & 12.

Cavaillé organ (1789), Saint-Guilhem le Désert.

BIGGS. *Historic Organs of Europe: France.* ***211**
Columbia MS-7438.

> BALBASTRE: Joseph est bien marié.
> CLERAMBAULT: Caprice sur les grands jeux (Suite II).
> F. COUPERIN: Offertoire (*Messe des couvents*); Fanfare, Rondeau,
> Bruit de guerre (*10ème ordre*).
> L. COUPERIN: Chaconnes (C, c, g, D).
> DANDRIEU: Noël "Or nous dites Marie"; Noël "Quand le Sauveur
> Jesus-Christ fut né de Marie."
> LEBEGUE: Basse de trompette (*Deuxième livre*).

Silbermann organs, Ebersmünster and Marmoutier.

BOYER and VILLARD. *Historische Clicquot-Orgeln in* ***212**
Frankreich.
Telefunken 6.35 293. 2 LPs.

> BOELY: Andante (b); Bin ich gleich von dir gewichen; Fantaisie et
> Fugue (Bb); Fugue; Quel étonnement; Suite; Le Vermeil du soleil;
> Voici la première entrée.

BOYVIN: *Premier Livre d'orgue.*

Clicquot organs:
St. Jacques-St. Christophe, Houdan; St. Nicolas-des-Champs, Paris.

CHAPUIS. *213
Astrée AS 20. (Also Telefunken 6.41 258 and Valois MB 872.)

CLERAMBAULT: Suites I and II.
DUMAGE: *Livre d'orgue.*

F.-H. Clicquot organ, Cathedral of Poitiers.

CHAPUIS. *Maîtres français de l'orgue.* 214
Charlin AMS 30 [1961]. (Also Schwann [Musica Sacra] 2530.)

DANDRIEU: Offertoire; Récit de nasard; Fugue sur "Ave maris stella"; Grand plein jeu.
GUILAIN: Suites, 1er et 2ème tons.
RAISON: Suite, premier ton (excerpts); Trio en passacaille (Suite, 2ème ton).

F.-H. Clicquot organ, Cathedral of Poitiers.

Reviews:
Organ Yearbook 3 (1972): 115-16; ibid., 8 (1977): 94.

CHAPUIS. *Noels of 18th-Century French Organists.* *215
Musical Heritage Society 324. (Duplicates Telefunken 6.41 260 and Valois MB 795.)

BALBASTRE: Prélude à la venue de Noël; Joseph est bien marié; Où s'en vont ces gais bergers; Au jo deu de pubelle; Grand dei, ribon ribeine.
DANDRIEU: A minuit fut fait un réveil; Quoy ma voisine es tu faché; Puer nobis nascitur; Allons voir ce divin Gage; Chantons de voix hautaine.
DAQUIN: Noël étranger; Noël en dialogue, duo, trio.

Koenig organ, St. Georges, Sarre-Union.

Review:
Organ Yearbook 3 (1972): 115.

CHAUVIN. *L'Orgue du Prytanée de la Flèche.*   ***216**
Da Camera SM 93205. (Also Oryx 1760.)

> DANDRIEU: Magnificat (e), excerpts; Suite (C), excerpts.
> RAISON: Messe, 6ème ton, excerpts; Messe, 8ème ton, excerpts.

Clicquot/Gonzalez organ, Military School of La Flèche.

DARASSE. *The Organ of the Mondaye Abbey.*   ***217**
Musical Heritage Society 3317. (Duplicates Arion ARN 90407.)

> LEBEGUE: Suite, 6ème ton; Magnificat, 4ème ton; Offertoire (F);
>   Elévation (G); Symphony (F).
> NIVERS: Suite du 2ème ton.

Organ:

> Anonymous builders (n.d.)/Verly and Parisot (1706-40)/Gonzalez
>   (1965).

DARASSE.   ***218**
Charlin AMS 18. (Also Schwann [Musica Sacra] 2 504.)

> D'ANGLEBERT: 5 fugues.
> RAISON: Messe, 3ème ton.

Faura organ (1764), Arles-sur-Tech.

Review:

> *Organ Yearbook* 8 (1977): 94.

DARASSE and ISOIR.   **219**
Turnabout TV 34074 [1968].

> COUPERIN: 2 Messes (*Paroisses* and *Couvents*).
> LEBEGUE: Magnificat, premier ton; selected pieces (*Deuxième Livre*).

Joyeuse/Gonzalez organ, Cathedral of Auch; the organ at Notre-Dame de
St. Etienne.

DARASSE and ISOIR. *16th-Century French Organ Music.*   **220**
See **36.**

DARASSE, ISOIR, and TERRASSE. *A Survey of the World's*   **221**
Greatest Organ Music: France, vol. 1—*"The Primitives."* See **37**.

DARASSE, ISOIR, and SAORGIN. *A Survey of the World's*   **222**
Greatest Organ Music: France, vol. 2.
Vox SVBX 5311. 3 LPs.

    G. CORRETTE: Messe, 8ᵉ ton.

    F. COUPERIN: *Messe des Paroisses:* Gloria couplets 1-3, 8, 9; *Messe des Couvents:* Kyrie couplets 2, 4; Gloria couplets 4, 6, 8; Offertoire; Benedictus; Elevation; Agnus (2 couplets).

    DORNEL: Prélude et fugue; Récit de tierce ou de nazard; Noël "Je me suis levé."

    GUILAIN: Suite, 2ᵉ ton (movements 1-6); Suite, 3ᵉ ton (movements 1-6); Suite, 4ᵉ ton; Basse de Cromorne.

    LASCEUX: Noël lorraine "Mes bonnes gens attendez-moi"; Fugue, Flûtes, Sinfonie concertante (Mass excerpts).

    LEBEGUE: Magnificat, 1ᵉʳ ton; Suite, 7ᵉ ton; Symphony (F); Offertoire "O filii et filiae; Noël "Où s'en vont ces gays bergers"; Noël "A la venue de noël."

Joyeuse/Gonzalez organ, Cathedral of Auch; the organ at Notre-Dame de St. Etienne.

NOTE: For volume 3 of *A Survey of the World's Greatest Organ Music: France,* see **257**.

DARASSE and SAORGIN. *A Survey of the World's Greatest*   ***223**
Organ Music: France, vol. 4.
Vox SVBX 5313. 3 LPs.

    CLERAMBAULT: Suites, 1ᵉʳ et 2ᵉ tons.
    D'AGINCOUR: Suites, 1ᵉʳ et 5ᵉ tons.
    D'ANGLEBERT: Allemande; Passacaille.
    DUMAGE: Suite, 1ᵉʳ ton.
    MARCHAND: Dialogue; Basse de cromhorne; Récit; Basse de trompette; Tierce en taille; Fugue; Basse de trompette; Quatuor; Récit; Fonds d'orgue; Dialogue; Te Deum.
    RAISON: Mass excerpts, 6ᵉ ton.

Clicquot organ (1717), Cathedral of Sarlat, Dordogne; Isnard (1786)/Cavaillé-Coll (1890)/Boisseai (1962) organ at St. Salomon-St. Grégoire, Pithiviers.

DOERR. *Orgelmusik des französischen Barock.*   ***224**
Christophorus SCGLX 75878.

> CLERAMBAULT: Suite, 2ème ton.
> M. CORRETTE: A la venue de noël; Vous qui désirez sans fin.
> F. COUPERIN: Gloria from *Messe des couvents.*
> DAQUIN: Noël en dialogue et en trio.
> GUILAIN: Grand jeu.

Silbermann organ, Marmoutier.

Review:

> *Organ Yearbook* 7 (1976): 176.

DURUFLE, M.   **225**
Voix de Son Maître C 063-10.754.

> F. COUPERIN: Kyrie, Gloria, Offertoire, Elevation, and Agnus Dei
> from *Messe des paroisses.*
> GRIGNY: Fugue à cinq, Duo, Récit de chromhorne, and Dialogue sur
> les grands jeux from "Veni creator"; Fugue à cinq, Récit du chant
> de l'hymne précédent from "Pange lingua."

DURUFLE, M.-M.   **226**
Voix de Son Maître C 063-10.545.

> CLERAMBAULT: Excerpts from Suites I and II.
> DAQUIN: Le Coucou; Noëls.

FROIDEBISE, P. *French Organ Masterpieces of the 17th and*   ***227**
18th Centuries.
Nonesuch H-71020 [1964].

> CLERAMBAULT: Plein jeu and Fugue from Suite I; Duo and Récit
> de nazard from Suite II.
> F. COUPERIN: Récit de tierce en taille.
> L. COUPERIN: Chaconnes (d, g).
> GRIGNY: Récit en taille (*Pange lingua*).
> MARCHAND: Dialogue sur les grands jeux; Récit; Plein jeu.
> PIROYE: Dialogue.

F. C. Schnitger organ (1723-26), Laurenskerk, Alkmaar.

GIL. *Noëls français à l'orgue.*   ***228**
Voix de Son Maître C 069-12.577.

>   BALBASTRE: Joseph est bien marié; Noëls bourguignons Nos. 4 &
>   5; Votre bonté, Grand Dieu.
>   BOELY: Noël en forme de pastorale.
>   M. CORRETTE: Carillon; Michaut qui causoit ce grand bruit; Noël
>   provençal; Tambourin; Où s'en vont ces gays bergers?
>   J. F. DANDRIEU: Chantons de voix hautaine.
>   DAQUIN: Noël X.

Isnard (1786)/Cavaillé-Coll (1890)/Boisseai (1962) organ at St. Salomon-St.
Grégoire, Pithiviers.

GIROD. *L'Orgue de Noël.*   **229**
Vogue SLVLX 416.

>   BALBASTRE: Joseph est bien marié.
>   CORRETTE: Vous qui désirez sans fin.
>   DANDRIEU: Noël de Saintonge; Or nous dites Marie; Quand le
>   sauveur Jésus-Christ.
>   DAQUIN: Noël.
>   LEBEGUE: Où s'en vont ces gays bergers.
>   TRADITIONAL: Dans une étable obscure; Entre le boeuf et l'âne gris;
>   Il est né le divin enfant; Mon beau sapin; O douce nuit.

GIROD. *L'Orgue français.*   **230**
Mondiodis CMDINT 9.812.

>   DANDRIEU: Musette; Offertoire.
>   DU MAGE: *Livre d'orgue.*
>   MARCHAND: Plein jeu.
>   NIVERS: Récit de voix humaine.
>   RACQUET: Fantaisie.
>   TITELOUZE: Verset on "Urbs Jerusalem."

GUILLOU.   **231**
Philips 836.850.

>   DANDRIEU: Noëls "Si c'est pour ôter la vie," "Adam où es-tu?", and
>   "Une bergère jolie."
>   DAQUIN: Noëls 1, 6, 9, 10, 12.
>   GUILLOU: Improvisations on traditional noels.

HANSEN. *Masterworks for Organ,* vol. 5: *17th- and 18th-*   ***232**
Century France.
Nonesuch H-71170.

> CLERAMBAULT: Suite, 2e ton.
> G. CORRETTE: Fond d'orgue.
> J.-F. DANDRIEU: Dialogue.
> DAQUIN: Noël suisse.
> GIGAULT: Préludes, 3e et 4e tons.
> JULLIEN: Prélude, 5e ton.
> LEBEGUE: Symphonie (D).
> RAISON: Quoniam tu solus.

Clicquot/Gonzalez organ, St. Merry, Paris.

ISOIR. *Cinq Siècles de l'orgue français.*   ***233**
Calliope 1.900.

A single-volume sampler from the entire period covered by the *Livre d'or* series. (See **235**ff.).

> ALAIN: Litanies.
> ATTAINGNANT: 3 versets du Te Deum.
> CLERAMBAULT: Caprice sur les grands jeux.
> F. COUPERIN: Kyrie et Fugue (*Messe des paroisses*); Tierce en taille;
>   Grand jeu (*Messe des couvents*).
> L. COUPERIN: Bransle de Basque.
> DAQUIN: Noël sur les jeux d'anches.
> FRANCK: Prélude (Fugue et Variation).
> GERVAISE: Bransles de Champagne et de Bourgogne.
> GRIGNY: Veni Creator, en taille à 5.
> GUILAIN: Basse de trompette, 1er ton.
> LASCEUX: Symphonie concertante.
> LEFEBURE-WELY: Sortie (Bb).
> WIDOR: Toccata (*Symphony V*).

Cavaillé-Coll organ, Cathedral of Luçon; Clicquot organs at Houdan, Palace of Fontainebleau, and Cathedral of Poitiers; Isnard organ, Basilica of Saint-Maximin; Héman/Thierry/Kern organ, Saint-Séverin, Paris; Koenig organs at Sarre-Union and Angers; Thierry/Clicquot organ, St. Germain-des-Prés, Paris; Isnard (1786)/Cavaillé-Coll (1890)/Boisseai (1962) organ at St. Salomon-St. Grégoire, Pithiviers.

ISOIR. *French Organ Music of the 17th Century.*   ***234**
Musical Heritage Society 4121.

BOURGES: Fantaisie.
DU MONT: Prélude No. 10 (d).
RACQUET: Fantaisie.
RICHARD: Prélude (d).
ROBERDAY: Fugues et Caprices Nos. 1, 2 (g, g).

Koenig organ, Angers.

ISOIR. *Le Livre d'or de l'orgue français,* vol. 1: *L'Orgue à la*   **235**
Renaissance. See **38**.

ISOIR. *Le Livre d'or de l'orgue français,* vol. 2: *Titelouze.*   **236**
See **40**.

ISOIR. *Le Livre d'or de l'orgue français,* vol. 3: *L'Orgue*   ***237**
français au XVIIème siècle.
Calliope 1.903. (Reissued as Musical Heritage Society 4121.)

ANONYMOUS: Ave maris stella; Fantaisie.
DE BOURGES: Fantaisie.
DE LA BARRE: Sarabande.
DUMONT: Pavane (d); Prélude No. 10 (d).
RACQUET: Fantaisie.
RICHARD: Prélude (d).
ROBERDAY: First Fugue and Caprice (g); Third Fugue and Caprice
    (C); Tenth Fugue (g); Twelfth Fugue (D).
TOMELIN: Duo.

Koenig organ, Angers.

ISOIR. *Le Livre d'or de l'orgue français,* vol. 4: *L'Orgue*   ***238**
français sous Louis XIV.
Calliope 1.904.

D'ANGLEBERT: 5 Fugues; Quatuor.
GIGAULT: Fugue à 3, 1er ton; Fugues, 1er et 3e tons; Fugue sur le
    Kyrie; Kyrie double; Tu solus altissimus.
JULLIEN: Suite, 1er ton.

Thierry/Clicquot organ, St. Germain-des-Prés, Paris.

ISOIR. *Le Livre d'or de l'orgue français,* vol. 5: *L'Orgue*   ***239**
français sous Louis XIV.
Calliope 1.905. (Duplicated by Musical Heritage Society 4202.)

> L. COUPERIN: Suite: Allemande, Sarabande en canon, Fantaisie,
> Chaconne (d), Bransle de Basque, Passacaille.
> GEOFFROY: Kyrie; Lucis Creator; La Marche; 2 Menuets; Offerte
> grave; Ouverture d'Isis.

Koenig organ, Angers.

ISOIR. *Le Livre d'or de l'orgue français,* vol. 6: *L'Orgue*   ***240**
français au grand siècle.
Calliope 1.906.

> BOYVIN: Suites, 1er et 4e tons (*Livre d'orgue II*).
> NIVERS: Suite, 4e ton.
> RAISON: Offerte . . . Vive le Roy.

Clicquot organ, St. Jacques, Compiègne.

ISOIR. *Le Livre d'or de l'orgue français,* vol. 10: *Grigny,*   ***241**
Lebègue.
Calliope 1.910.

> GRIGNY: Messe, part one.
> LEBEGUE: Suite, 2e ton; Elévation; Sinfonie (Bb).

Clicquot organ, Poitiers Cathedral.

ISOIR. *Le Livre d'or de l'orgue français,* vol. 14: *Dandrieu,*   ***242**
DuMage.
Calliope 1.914.

> DANDRIEU: Excerpts from *Premier Livre d'orgue.*
> DUMAGE: *Premier Livre d'orgue.*

Clicquot organ, Palace of Fontainebleau.

ISOIR. *Le Livre d'or de l'orgue français,* vol. 15: *Clérambault,*   ***243**
G. Corrette.
Calliope 1.915.

    CLERAMBAULT: Suites I and II.

    G. CORRETTE. Dialogue de voix humaine; Dessus de tierce par ac-
    cords; Dialogue à 2 choeurs.

Clicquot organ, Palace of Fontainebleau.

ISOIR. *Le Livre d'or de l'orgue français,* vol. 16: *Noëls français*   ***244**
au XVIIIème siècle.
Calliope 1.916.

    BALBASTRE: Quand Jesus naquit à noël.

    BEAUVARLET-CHARPENTIER: Noël en grand choeur.

    M. CORRETTE: Noël provençal.

    DANDRIEU: Chantons de voix hautaine; Joseph est bien marié; Si c'est
    pour être la vie.

    DAQUIN: Noël en récit de taille; Noël sur les jeux d'anches; Noël sur
    les flûtes.

Héman/Thierry/Kern organ, St. Séverin, Paris.

NOTE: For volumes 7, 8, 9, 11, 12, and 13 of this series, see *Individual Composer*
listings, **282, 307, 314,** and **324.**

In addition to the individual issues of the *Livre d'or* series listed above, Calliope of-
fers the following options.

ISOIR. *Le Livre d'or de l'orgue français: Les Précurseurs.*   **245**
See **39.**

ISOIR. *Le Livre d'or de l'orgue français: Le Grand Siècle.*   ***246**
Calliope 190 406. 3 LPs combining the contents of volumes 4-6
(1.904-1.906). See **238, 239, 240.**

ISOIR. *Le Livre d'or de l'orgue français: Couperin; Marchand.*   ***247**
Calliope 190 709. 3 LPs combining the contents of volumes 7-9
(1.907-1.909). See **282** and **324.**

ISOIR. *Le Livre d'or de l'orgue français: Grigny; Lebègue.*   ***248**
Calliope 191 012. 3 LPs combining the contents of volumes 10-12
(1.910-1.912). See **241** and **307**.

ISOIR. *Le Livre d'or de l'orgue français: Le Siècle de Louis XV.*   ***249**
Calliope 191 315. 3LPs combining the contents of volumes 13-15
(1.913-1.915). See **242, 243, 314**.

ISOIR and THIRY. *Le Livre d'or de l'orgue français.*   ***250**
Calliope 190 130. 30 LPs combining the complete contents of the
individual records in this set (1.901-1.930). Isoir is the performer for volumes
1-24, Thiry for volumes 25-30. The repertory covers the 16th through 20th
centuries and ends with Messiaen's *Livre d'orgue.*

KLEIN. *Orgelmusik aus Marienmünster.*   ***251**
Fono Schallplatten Münster FSM 43 5 03.

> L. COUPERIN: 2 Sarabandes (c, d); 2 Chaconnes (C, g); Passacaille
> (g); Pastourelle (d); Fantaisie (g); Duo (g); Branle de Basque (F).
> DU MAGE: *Livre d'orgue.*

Patroklus-Möller organ.

MARCHAL. *The Art of André Marchal,* vol. 2: *Masters of*   **252**
French Organ Music.
Unicorn UNLP 1047 [1956].

> F. COUPERIN: Offertoire (*Messe des paroisses*).
> L. COUPERIN: Chaconne (g).
> DAQUIN: Noël I.
> GRIGNY: Veni Creator Spiritus.
> LEBEGUE: Les Cloches.
> MARCHAND: Fond d'orgue.
> TITELOUZE: Magnificat.

Holtkamp organ, Massachusetts Institute of Technology. Assisted by the
M.I.T. choir, dir. Liepmann.

MARCHAL. *Maîtres français des XVIIᵉ et XVIIIᵉ siècles.*   **253**
I.M.E. Pathé Marconi LUM 3.101.

> CLERAMBAULT: Suite du 2ᵉ ton.
> L. COUPERIN: Chaconne (g).
> DAQUIN: Noël.
> GRIGNY: Récit de tierce en taille.
> LEBEGUE: Les Cloches.
> MARCHAND: Basse de trompette.

MARCHAL, organ; REIMS CATHEDRAL CHOIR, dir.   ***254**
MUZERELLE. *Christmas in the Great Cathedral of Reims.*
Musical Heritage Society 818. (Duplicates Erato STU 70 339.)

Organ works:
> BALBASTRE: Joseph est bien marié.
> DANDRIEU: Puer nobis nascitur.
> DAQUIN: Noëls I and VIII.

Choral works by:
> COSTELEY, GASTOLDI, GEOFFRAY, GEVAERT, LITAIZE,
> PAGOT, PERISSAS, PRAETORIUS, and RAMEAU.

Organ, Cathedral of Reims.

NARDIN and PIERRE.   **255**
Studios S.M. 33-45.

> BOYVIN: Grand dialogue; Voix humaine; Fugue chromatique;
> Cromorne; Prélude à 2 choeurs; Basse de trompette; Fond d'orgue;
> Trio à 2 dessus; Tierce en taille; Grand dialogue.
> F. COUPERIN: Benedictus from *Messe des couvents;* Dialogue sur la
> voix humaine from *Messe des paroisses.*
> DU MAGE: Grand jeu.
> GRIGNY: Tierce en taille; Veni Creator.

PIERRE.   **256**
RCA RFL 10.031.

> BALBASTRE: Noël "Joseph est bien marié."
> CLERAMBAULT: Suite du 1ᵉʳ ton; Suite du 2ᵉ ton.

J.-F. DANDRIEU: Noëls "Une bergère jolie" and "Chantons de voix
hautaine"; Noël poitevin; Noël de Saintonge; Or nous dîtes Marie.

Lefebvre organ/restored by Haerpfer and Ermann (1971-72), Caudebec-en-
Caux.

Review:

Music/The AGO and RCCO Magazine 10/7 (July 1976): 12.

RAYNAUD, SAORGIN, and TERRASSE. *A Survey of the*   ***257**
World's Greatest Organ Music: France, vol. 3.
Vox SVBX 5312. 3 LPs.

BALBASTRE: A la venue de Noël.
BOYVIN: Prélude, 2ᵉ ton; Trio à 2 dessus, 2ᵉ ton; Duo, 2ᵉ ton;
Cromorne en taille, 4ᵉ ton; Basse de trompette, 7ᵉ ton; Tierce en
taille, 5ᵉ ton; Dialogue en fugue, 4ᵉ ton; Prélude, 5ᵉ ton; Duo, 4ᵉ
ton; Quatuor, 5ᵉ ton; Dialogue de trompette avec cornet séparé,
7ᵉ ton; Fugue chromatique, 4ᵉ ton; Dialogue en fugue, 8ᵉ ton; Tierce
en taille, 4ᵉ ton; Grand dialogue à 4 choeurs.
DANDRIEU: Magnificats (D, d, and g); Trio; Duo en cor de chasse;
Offerte; Récit de nazard; Fugue sur . . . Exultet; Tierce en taille;
Basse de trompette; Cromorne en taille; Dialogue; Noël "Carillon
en cloches"; Noël "Chantons de voix hautaine."
DAQUIN: Noëls Nos. 6, 7, 8.
GIGAULT: Et in terra pax; Récit de cromorne en taille; Fugue à 3 sur
l'Agnus; Prélude, 1ᵉʳ ton.
GRIGNY: Veni Creator; Mass excerpts.
NIVERS: Suites, 1ᵉʳ, 5ᵉ, et 7ᵉ tons.

Clicquot/Gonzalez organ, St. Merry, Paris; Isnard (1786)/Cavaillé-Coll
(1890)/Boisseai (1962) organ at St. Salomon-St. Grégoire, Pithiviers; organ
at Notre-Dame de St. Etienne.

SMITH. *A Treasury of Early French Organ Music:*   **258**
Variations on French Noëls.
Cambridge CRM 505 [1962].

P. DANDRIEU: Puer nobis nascitur; Quand je m'éveillai; Grâce soit
rendue à Dieu; Sortons de nos chaumines; Où s'en vont ces gays
bergers?
DAQUIN: Noël "Grand jeu et duo"; Noël sur les flûtes; Noël suisse.

LEBEGUE: A la venue de Noël; Noël cette journée; Une vierge pucelle; Noël pour l'amour de Marie; Or nous dîtes, Marie; Laissez paistre vos bestes.

A. Silbermann organ (1709-10), enlarged by J. A. Silbermann (1746), restored by Muhleisen and Kern (1955), Marmoutier.

TAMBYEFF. *Christmas Music for Organ: Noels of the Great*   ***259**
17th- and 18th-Century French Masters.
Musical Heritage Society 3511. (Duplicates Arion 90427.)

BALBASTRE: Divine princesse; Fanne coriage, le diable â mor; Qué tu grojan, quel folie; Votre bonté grand Dieu.
M.-A. CHARPENTIER: Joseph est bien marié.
DANDRIEU: Chantons de voix hautaine; Laissez paistre vos bestes; Noël poitevin.
DAQUIN: Noël suisse.
DORNEL: Je me suis levé.
LASCEUX: Noël lorrain.
LEBEGUE: Les Bourgeoises de Châtre; Les Cloches.

St. Eustache, Paris.

TAYLOR.   **260**
Elysée SD 1001.

J.-F. DANDRIEU: *Premier Livre d'orgue:* Dialogue, Basse de trompette, Tierce en taille, Concert de flûtes, Musète, Duo en cor de chasse sur la trompette, Offertoire, Marqué, Suite de l'offertoire.
DUMAGE: *Livre d'orgue.*

Fisk organ, Old West Church, Boston.

VER HASSELT. *Couperins Orgel zu St. Gervais.*   ***261**
Da Camera 93 203.

BALBASTRE: Qué tu grojan.
CLERAMBAULT: Suite du 1er ton.
F. COUPERIN: *Messe des paroisses:* Kyrie I, Duo sur les tierces, voix humaine; *Messe des couvents:* Récit de cornet, Cromorne en taille.
L. COUPERIN: Chaconne (F).

D'AGINCOURT: Suite, 2e ton.
GRIGNY: Tierce en taille.

St. Gervais, Paris.

This seems to replace an earlier recording by the same performer with similar contents: M3203.

VER HASSELT, organ; LA CECILIENNE. *Weihnachtslieder aus*   ***262**
Frankreich.
Da Camera 194 021.

Organ works:
BEAUVARLET-CHARPENTIER: Où s'en vont ces gays bergers.
BOELY: Je me suis levé.
BRUNOLD: Ciel versez.
DAQUIN: Adam fut un pauvre homme.
GEOFFROY: Noël nouvelet.

Various noëls sung by La Cécilienne.

WILLS, A. *Ely Cathedral.*   ***263**
Saga 5433/4. 2 LPs.

DAQUIN: 12 Noëls.
MARCHAND: Basse de cromhorne; 2 Dialogues; Duo, Fugue, Grand jeu, Plein jeu; Quatuor; Tierce en taille.

Ely Cathedral organ.

Review:
The Organ 55/219 (January 1977): 147-48.

Individual Composers

Balbastre, Claude

ALAIN. *13 Noëls.*   ***263.1**
Erato STU 71119.

Organ of anonymous origins, rebuilt by Callinet and restored by Kern, Cathedral of Uzès.

SAORGIN. *13 Noëls.*   ***263.2**
Harmonia Mundi 984.

Serassi organ (1807), Tende.

Boyvin, Jacques

HEUDRON.   **264**
Voix de Son Maître C 065 -12.061.

Livre d'orgue (1700):
  Suites, 2ᵉ, 3ᵉ, 4ᵉ, et 7ᵉ tons.

TERRASSE. *L'Encyclopédie de l'orgue,* vol. 44.   **265**
Erato EDO 242.

Livre d'orgue (1689):
  Suites, 1ᵉʳ, 4ᵉ, et 7ᵉ tons (excerpts).

Livre d'orgue (1700):
  Suites, 2ᵉ, 4ᵉ, 5ᵉ, et 8ᵉ tons.

VILLARD.   ***266**
Stil discothèque 1.803.

Premier Livre d'orgue (1689):
  Suites du 1ᵉʳ au 8ᵉ tons.

Clérambault, Louis-Nicolas
Complete Works

BROSSE, organ and harpsichord.   ***267**
EMI—Voix de Son Maître 2 C 069- 16330. 2 LPs.

Complete organ works plus 2 harpsichord suites (C, c).

Organ at the Cathedral of Sainte-Marie de Saint-Bertrand de Comminges;
Kroll harpsichord, Belbèze chateau, Comminges.

Review:
  Le Courrier musical de France 69 (1980): 20.

FOCCROULLE. *Premier Livre d'orgue.*   ***268**
Mixtur MM 50 019.

Clicquot organ, Houdan.

GILBERT. *First Organ Book.*   ***269**
Musical Heritage Society 1688. (Duplicates Harmonia Mundi 964 and
Oryx 1737.)

Beckerath organ, St. Joseph's Oratory, Montreal.

LITAIZE, organ; MESPLE, soprano. *Musique de Clérambault.*   ***270**
Voix de Son Maître C 065-12.589.

Organ works:
 Premier Livre d'orgue.
Motets for voice and organ.

MARCHAL. *First Organ Book.*   ***271**
Musical Heritage Society 640.

Joyeuse/Gonzalez organ, Cathedral of Auch.

PIERRE. *Premier Livre d'orgue.*   **272**
RCA FR FRL 1.0031.

WEIR. *First Organ Book.*   ***273**
Argo ZRG 742.

Prädiger-Kirche, Zürich.

Corrette, Gaspard

CHAPUIS. *Orgues historiques,* vol. 25: *Marmoutier.*   **274**
Musique de Tous les Temps OH 25 [1963]. A 45-rpm record
accompanied by a multi-page booklet (in French) on the organ.

Messe du 8ᵉ ton:
> Kyrie I; Dessus de tierce par accords; Dialogue de voix humaine; Récit
> tendre; Prélude à 2 choeurs; Concert pour les flûtes; Cromorne en
> taille; Dialogue à 2 choeurs.

Silbermann organ, Marmoutier.

DAVELUY. *Mass, Mode 8.*   ***275**
Musical Heritage Society 1430. (Duplicates Oryx 1736.)

Beckerath organ, St. Joseph's Oratory, Montreal.

FARRELL. *Mass, Mode 8.*   **276**
Mastertone M1205.

Holtkamp organ, St. John's University Church, Collegeville, Minnesota.

VILLARD. *L'Encyclopédie de l'orgue,* vol. 26.   **277**
Erato EDO 226.

> Messe du 8ᵉ ton.

Clicquot organ, Cathedral of Poitiers.

Couperin, François
Complete Works

ALAIN. *Messe à l'usage des paroisses; Messe propre pour les*   ***278**
couvents.
Musical Heritage Society 1881/2. 2 LPs. (Duplicates Erato EDO 222/223:
L'Encyclopédie de l'orgue, vols. 22-23 [1969].)

Clicquot organ, Cathedral of Poitiers.

BARDON.   ***279**
Verany PV 1801/2 [1980?]. 2 LPs.

Isnard/Chéron organ, Saint-Maximin-du-Var.

Review:
> *Le Courrier musical de France* 70 (1980): 63.

CHAPUIS. *280

Harmonia Mundi 714/15 [1967]. 2 LPs. (HM 714 is No. 1 in the Harmonia Mundi series: *Orgues historiques: Le Monde de l'orgue.* The two volumes have also been reissued by RCA: VICS 6018.)

Isnard organ (1772), Saint-Maximin (Provence).

COCHEREAU, organ; CHOIR OF ST. PAUL'S, PARIS. 281

L'Oiseau Lyre OLS 161/63. 3 LPs.

This stereo release seems to supersede a monaural recording from the 1960s: OL 50155/57.

ISOIR. *Le Livre d'or de l'orgue français,* vols. 7-8. *282

Calliope 1.907/8. 2 LPs.

Thierry/Clicquot organ at St. Germain-des-Prés, Paris; Koenig organ at Sarre-Union.

KOOPMAN. *283

Telefunken 6.35415. 2 LPs.

Clicquot organ at Houdan.

LEFEBVRE. *284

FY 053/54 [1977]. 2 LPs.

St. Gervais, Paris.

LITAIZE. *285

Voix de Son Maître C167 -14.035/36. 2 LPs [1976].

Notre-Dame de Caudebec-en-Caux.

NOEHREN. *286

Lyrichord LLST 7130. 2 LPs.

Noehren organs, Collingwood Presbyterian Church, Toledo, Ohio, and First Presbyterian Church, Deerfield, Illinois.

ROBERT.   *287
Charlin CL9 [1964-65]. 2 LPs. (Duplicated by Schwann [Musica Sacra] AMS 74/75.)

Contains both masses plus the following works by L. COUPERIN:
    Allemande; Sarabande en canon; Chaconne (g).

Clicquot/Gonzalez organ, St. Merry, Paris.

The *Messe des couvents* is also reissued on Nonesuch H-71150.

ROGG.   *288
Voix de Son Maître C165 -04.963/64. 2 LPs [1973].

Silbermann organ, Marmoutier.

VEIR.   *289
Argo/Decca 4BBA 1011/2. 2 LPs.

Prädiger Kirche, Zürich.

Couperin, François
A Single Mass or Excerpts

CHAPUIS. *Orgues historiques*, vol. 23: *Le Petit-Andely*.   290
Musique de Tous les Temps OH 23 [1963]. A 45-rpm record accompanied by a multi-page booklet (in French) on the organ.

    Gloria couplets 3-6, 8; Sanctus (from *Messe des couvents*.)

Ingout organ, Le Petit Andely.

FESPERMAN. *Messe à l'usage des paroisses*.   *291
Cambridge CRS 2504 [1973].

Fisk organ, Old West Church, Boston.

JACQUENOD. *Messe à l'usage des couvents*.   *292
Studios S.M. 416.

MARCHAL. *Messe à l'usage des paroisses.*   ***293**
Musical Heritage Society 692 [1966]. (A reissue of an Erato release.)
Clicquot/Gonzalez organ, Military Academy at La Flèche.

Couperin, Louis

CHAPUIS, organ; BLANCHARD VOCAL ENSEMBLE; OBOE   **294**
ENSEMBLE; CONSORT OF VIOLS. *Unbekannte Werke Louis
Couperin.*
Deutsche Grammophon (Archive) ARC 198.361 [1966].

Organ works:
   Nos. 9, 10, 12, 13, 22, 23, 25-27, 31-33, 50, 53, 56-59, 68, 69 (from
   Pièces pour orgue).

Other works:
   2 Fantaisies sur le jeu des hautbois (D); Suite pour le clavecin (a);
   2 Fantaisies pour violes (G).

Clicquot organ of 1782 at Souvigny.

See also **287**.

Dandrieu, Jean-François

ALAIN.   ***295**
Musical Heritage Society 1535.

   Magnificat, Suite V (1st verset); Duo sur la trompette, Suite IV; Duet,
   Suite VI; Flutes, Suite IX; Basse et dessus de trompette, Suite VIII;
   Trio, Suite VII; Duo de cor de chasse, Suite II; Dialogue, Suite X.

Gonzalez organ, Cathedral of Meaux.

HEUDRON. *Historische Orgeln der Pfalz.*   ***296**
Unisono Pfeifer-Koch 22 477.

   Selected noëls.

Organs at Bergzabern, Mühlheim/Eis, Kallstadt, and Mutterstadt.

Daquin, Louis-Claude

ALAIN. *12 Noëls.*   *297
Erato STU 71.118 [1976].

Organ of anonymous origins/rebuilt by Callinet and restored by Kern, Cathedral of Uzès.

BIGGS. *12 Noels.*   *298
Columbia M32735 (formerly ML 5567 [1960?]).

Flentrop organ, Busch-Reisinger Museum, Harvard University.

CHAPUIS. *Orgues historiques. Le Monde de l'orgue No. 8:*   *299
Marmoutier.
Harmonia Mundi HM 531.

    Noels 6, 8-12.

Silbermann organ (1710), Marmoutier.

JACQUENOD.   *300
Studios S.M. B-433.

    Noels 4, 5, 7, and 9-12.

LITAIZE. *12 Noëls.*   *301
Voix de Son Maître C 069-12.814. (Duplicates Connoisseur CS 2125.)

Notre-Dame de Caudebec-en-Caux.

Dornel, Louis-Antoine

SAORGIN. *Orgues historiques,* vol. 20: *Saint-Chinian.*   302
Musique de Tous les Temps HM 4510 [1968]. A 45-rpm record accompanied by a multi-page booklet (in French) on the organ.

    Prélude; Duo; Basse et dessus de trompette; Cornet; Basse de voix humaine; Fonds d'orgue; Dialogue; Trio; Récit; Basse de cromhorne.

Grigny, Nicolas de
Complete Works

ALAIN. *Livre d'orgue.*   *303
Erato STU 71381/82. 2 LPs [1980].

Carouge/Prade/Dunand organ, Abbey Church, La Chaise-Dieu.

ALAIN. *Livre d'orgue.*   *304
Musical Heritage Society 735/36. (Duplicates Erato: *Encyclopédie de l'orgue,* vols. 27-28 [1965].) 2 LPs.

Clicquot/Haerpfer-Erman organ, Cathedral of Sarlat, Dordogne.

CHAPUIS. *Livre d'orgue.*   305
Astrée 8/9. (Duplicated by Telefunken 6.42 327 and 6.42 228.) 2 LPs.

Valtrin/Callinet/Schwenkedel organ, Basilique St-Christophe, Belfort.

GRUNENWALD. *Livre d'orgue.*   306
Vega 8.701/2/3. 3 LPs.

Clicquot organ, Cathedral of Poitiers.

ISOIR. *Le Livre d'or de l'orgue français,* vols. 11-12.   *307
Calliope 1.911/12. 2 LPs.

Together with partial contents of volume 10 of this series (see **241**), these records contain the complete works of Grigny. The 5 Hymns from Calliope 1.912 are reissued on Musical Heritage Society 4079.

Clicquot organ, Cathedral of Poitiers; Isnard organ (1772), Saint-Maximin de Provence.

LEFEBVRE. *Livre d'orgue.*   *307.1
FY 075/76. 2 LPs.

ROGG. *Livre d'orgue.*   *308
Voix de Son Maître C 167 -12.887/88. 2 LPs [1973].

St.-Salomon/St-Grégoire, Pithiviers.

SMITH, M. *Livre d'orgue.*   309
Valois 425/6/7. 3 LPs.

Silbermann organ, Marmoutier.

Awarded the *Grand prix du disque,* 1961.

Grigny, Nicolas de
Selected Works

FESPERMAN. *Organ Works.*   *310
Orion ORS 76253.

  Mass; 2 Hymns: Verbum supernum; Veni Creator

Fisk organ, University of Vermont.

Review:
  Music/The AGO and RCCO Magazine 11/4 (April 1977): 12.

SAORGIN.   *311
Turnabout TV 4054 and TV 34054S.

  Mass selections; 2 hymns: Pange lingua; Veni Creator.

Notre-Dame de St. Etienne.

Guilain, Jean-Adam-Guillaume
Complete Works

ALAIN. *Encyclopédie de l'orgue,* vol. 54: *Guilain: Pièces pour*   *312
orgue.
Erato EDO 254 [1972].

Valtrin/Callinet/Schwenkedel organ, Basilique St-Christophe, Belfort.

HEUDRON.   **313**
Voix de Son Maître C 065 -12.062 [1971].

Cathédrale de Saint-Pierre, Saintes.

ISOIR.   ***314**
Musical Heritage Society 3977. (Duplicates Calliope 1.913: *Le Livre
d'or de l'orgue français,* vol. 13.)

Clicquot organ, Houdan.

JACQUENOD. *Orgues historiques. Le Monde de l'orgue No. 7:*   ***315**
Taizé.
Harmonia Mundi 1.206.

Ahrend organ (1974), Taizé.

RÜBSAM.   ***316**
Da Camera 93 263. (Duplicates Spectrum SR-102.)

Rieger organ, Abbey Church of Marienstatt.

Lebègue, Nicolas

ALAIN.   ***317**
Erato STU 70.950 [1974].

> Les Cloches; Offertoire sur "O Filii"; Magnificat du 1er ton; Tierce
> en taille de la 6ème suite; Symphonie sur le bémol Fa; Suite de 2ème
> ton; Excerpts from Suite du 1er ton.

Lefebvre/Haerpfer-Erman, Eglise Notre-Dame, Caudebec-en-Caux.

ISOIR. *Le Livre d'or de l'orgue français,* vol. 10. See **241**.   **318**

PIERRONT. *L'Oeuvre d'orgue de Lebègue.*   **319**
Schwann (Musica Sacra) AMS-1 [1961-?].

Messe (complete); Magnificat, 3ᵉ ton; Noël "Pour l'amour de Marie"; Symphonie (Bv); 2 offertoires; Stabat Mater; O filii et filiae.

Clicquot/Gonzalez organ, St. Merry, Paris.

Marchand, Louis
Complete Works

TAYLOR. *Complete Organ Works.*   **320**
Sound Dynamics Associates 1005/6. 2 LPs.

Fisk organ, Old West Church, Boston.

Marchand, Louis
Selected Works

ALAIN.   ***321**
Erato STU 70949 [1974].

> *Premier Livre d'orgue* (complete); Récit, Fond d'orgue, Récit et Grand jeu (*Livre II*); Fugue, En taille (*Livre IV*); Basse de trompette, Plein jeu, Fugue, Tierce en taille (*Livre V*).

Lefebvre/Haerpfer-Erman organ, Eglise Notre-Dame, Caudebec-en-Caux.

CHAPUIS. *Orgues historiques. Le Monde de l'orgue No. 6:*   ***322**
Souvigny.
Harmonia Mundi 532 [1975]. (Formerly HMO 30.532. Duplicated by Oryx 1754.)

> *Premier Livre d'orgue* (complete); *Pièces diverses:* Pièce (e), Récit de voix humaine, Pièce (a), Plein jeu, and Cromorne en taille.

Clicquot organ (1782), Souvigny.

ISOIR. *First Organ Book.*   ***323**
Musical Heritage Society 4174.

Isnard organ (1773), restored by Gonzalez (1953), Saint-Maximin en Provence.

ISOIR. *Le Livre d'or de l'orgue français,* vol. 9.   ***324**
Calliope 1.909.

> *Livres d'orgue* I and III (complete); excerpts from *Livres d'orgue* II and V.

Isnard organ (1773), restored by Gonzalez (1953), Saint-Maximin en Provence.

WEIR.   ***325**
Argo ZK 57. (Also 7.331.)

Livre I:

> Tierce en taille, Récit de nazard, Basse de trompette ou de cromorne, Dialogue.

Livre III:

> Grand dialogue (C).

Livre IV:

> Complete.

Livre V:

> Complete.

Nivers, Guillaume-Gabriel

ISOIR. *Encyclopédie de l'orgue,* vol. 46.   **326**
Erato EDO 246.

Livre d'orgue:

> Suite, 1er ton.

Second Livre d'orgue:

> Te Deum.

Troisième Livre d'orgue:

> Suites, 2e, 5e, et 7e tons.

Roberday, François
Complete Works

CHAPUIS. *12 Fugues et 6 caprices sur le même sujet.*   ***327**
Astrée-Valois AS 14.

WEIR. *12 Fugues et 6 caprices sur le même sujet.*   ***328**
Argo ZRG 744.

Roberday, François
Selected Works

CHAPUIS. *Orgues historiques,* vol. 27: *L'Isle-sur-la-Sorgue.*   **329**
Musique de Tous les Temps [1963]. 7″ LP, 33 rpm record
accompanied by a multi-page booklet (in French) on the organ.

> Fugues II, III, XII.

Le Royer organ (1648), L'Isle-sur-la-Sorgue (Provence).

CHAPUIS. *Orgues historiques: L'Isle-sur-la-Sorgue et Manosque.*   **330**
Harmonia Mundi 530 (formerly HMO 30.530).

> Fugue cinquième; Fugue troisième et caprice sur le même sujet; Fugue
> deuxième et caprice sur le même sujet; Fugue douzième; Fugue
> première et caprice sur le même sujet; Fugue huitième et caprice sur
> le même sujet; Fugue dixième.

Le Royer organ (1648), L'Isle-sur-la-Sorgue; Esprit Meysonnier organ (1625),
l'Eglise St-Sauveur, Manosque (Provence).

Titelouze, Jehan

See **40**.

CHAPTER 13
GERMANY AND AUSTRIA

Anthologies

ALAIN. *L'Encyclopédie de l'orgue,* vol. 56: *L'Orgue nordique.*   **331**
Erato EDO 256 [1973].

> BRUHNS: Complete organ works.
> BRUNKHORST: Prelude and Fugue (e).
> KNELLER: Prelude and Fugue (d).
> LEYDING: Prelude (E♭).

Marcussen organ, Cathedral of Viborg, Denmark.

ANTONINI. *Gloire de l'orgue baroque.*   ***332**
Arion 37 191.

> FROBERGER: Toccata capriccio.
> FUX: Sonata sexta.
> KERLL: Canzona; Toccata tutta de salti.
> GEORG MUFFAT: Passacaille.
> PACHELBEL: Fantasia.
> PASQUINI: Toccata settima.
> WECKMANN: Canzon.

Organ at Malaucène: Charles Boisselin (1712)/Joseph Isnard (1784).

BIBO. *Pape-Orgeldokumente,* vol. 12: *Orgel in der Valentinus-*   ***333**
Kirche Kiedrich.
Fono Schallplatten Münster 63 712.

> BACH: Präludium (C), S. 553; Wer nur den lieben Gott lässt walten,
> S. 642.

FISCHER: Christ ist erstanden; Komm, heiliger Geist.
PACHELBEL: Vom Himmel kam der Engel Schar.
ZIPOLI: Pastorale.

In addition to these pieces, organ improvisations demonstrate the individual stops of the organ. The organ, which contains some late medieval pipework, goes back to the end of the 15th century or earlier and was rebuilt in the 17th century and again in the 19th century (by Hooghuys). Restoration by Oberlinger (1970/71).

Reviews:
Ars organi 25/54 (October 1977): 255; *Musik und Kirche* 47/1 (January-February): 33.

BIGGS. *Famous Organs of Holland and Northern Germany.*   *334
See **742.**

BIGGS. *The Golden Age of the Organ: Historic Organs of*   *335
Holland and Germany.
Columbia M2S 697 (formerly M2L 297; also ML 5955/56 [1964].) 2 LPs.

BACH: 8 Little Preludes and Fugues; Concerto V (after Vivaldi); Toccata (d), S. 565; Prelude and Fugue (d), S. 538; 6 pieces from the *Anna Magdalena Bach Book.*
CIMELLO: Canzona villanesca.
PEPPING: 7 chorale preludes.
SCHEIN: Aus Venuskränzlein.
WALTHER: Partita on "Meinen Jesum lass ich nicht."

12 Schnitger organs: Alkmaar, Cappel, Dedesdorf, Ganderkesee, Hamburg (Jakobikirche), Lüdingworth, Neuenfelde, Norden, Stade, Steinkirchen, Uithuizen, and Zwolle.

CHAPELET. *Orgues des Baléares,* vol. 2.   *336
Harmonia Mundi HM 949.

BÖHM: Christ lag in Todesbanden.
FISCHER: 4 Ricercari.
PACHELBEL: Ricercar (C).
SCHEIDEMANN: Ach Gott, vom Himmel sieh darein; Durch Adams Fall ist ganz verderbt; Es ist das Heil uns kommen her.

SCHEIDT: Von der Fortuna.
SWEELINCK: Balletto del gran Ducca; Fantasia cromatica; Von der
Fortuna.

Caimari/Bosch organ (18th c.), Convent Sant-Geroni, Palma de Mallorca.

CHAPUIS. *N. Bruhns: L'Oeuvre d'orgue. J. N. Hanff: Les* ***337**
Six Chorals.
Valois MB 835 [1974].

BRUHNS: Complete works.
HANFF: Complete works.

Kern organ, Eglise St. Maximin, Thionville.

Reviews:

Organ Yearbook 3 (1972): 115; *Music/The AGO and RCCO Magazine*
10/3 (March 1976): 3.

COSTA. *Les Grands Maîtres baroques avant J. S. Bach,* 2 vols. ***338**
Musidisc RC 16.014. 2 LPs.

VOL. 1.
Maîtres baroques de l'Allemagne du nord:
BÖHM: Prelude and Fugue (C).
BRUHNS: 2 Preludes and Fugues (e, e).
BUXTEHUDE: Herr Christ, der einig Gottes Sohn; In dulci jubilo; Nun
komm der Heiden Heiland; Prelude and Fugue (g).
LÜBECK: Prelude and Fugue (E).

VOL. 2.
Maîtres baroques de l'Allemagne du sud:
KRIEGER: Toccata and Fugue (a).
GEORG MUFFAT: Passacaglia (g); Toccata XI.
PACHELBEL: Vom Himmel hoch; Chaconne (f); Fugue (C); Toccata.
SPETH: Toccata I.

DANBY. *Christmas Organ Music from Old Germany.* **339**
Pye-Virtuoso TPLS 13034.

BACH: Fantasia (G); Nun komm, der Heiden Heiland.
BRUHNS: Prelude and Fugue (G).

    BUXTEHUDE: Puer natus in Bethlehem; Wie schön leuchtet der
      Morgenstern.
    LÜNEBURG TABLATURE: Selected pieces.
    SCHLICK: Maria zart.
    SICHER TABLATURE: Selected pieces.

Marienkirche, Lemgo; the instrument dates back to the 16th century but was
frequently rebuilt, including a complete rebuilding by Klassmeyer in 1887.
Restored by Paul Ott in two stages (1950 and 1961).

Review:
    Organ Yearbook 7 (1976): 172-73.

DANBY. *Nicholas Danby at the Organ of Marienkirche,*   **340**
Lemgo, Germany.
Pye-Virtuoso TPLS 13056.

    BUXTEHUDE: Präludien und Fugen (D, fc).
    LÜNEBURG TABLATURE: Ein feste Burg; Herr Jesu Christ, dich zu
      uns wend.
    PACHELBEL: Aria Sebaldina; Wie schön leuchtet der Morgenstern.
    RITTER: Sonatina (d).
    SCHEIDT: Allein Gott in der Höh sei Ehr.
    SWEELINCK: Echo Fantasia (a).

For organ information, see **339**.

Review:
    Organ Yearbook 7 (1976): 172-73.

DE KLERK. *Die alte Orgel: Arp Schnitger-Orgeln von Stein-*   **341**
kirchen und Neuenfelde.
Telefunken SAWT 9412-B.

    BUXTEHUDE: Praeludium und Fuge (F).
    M. PRAETORIUS: Vater unser.
    SCHEIDEMANN: Magnificat-Fantasie (8th mode).
    SCHEIDT: Da Jesus an dem Kreuze stund.
    SWEELINCK: Echofantasie.

Schnitger organs in the Ev. Pfarrkirche, Steinkirchen, and in St. Pankratius,
Neuenfelde. The Steinkirchen organ was a Schnitger "rebuild" of an earlier
organ by Dirck Hoyer. The Neuenfelde organ dates from 1683-88 and was
rebuilt by Paul Ott in 1938. Both instruments were restored by von Beckerath,
in 1946-48 and in 1952-56 respectively.

This record has been released as part of a two-record album entitled *Die Orgel-Serie: Norddeutsche Arp-Schnitger-Orgeln,* TK 11521/1-2 and 6.35054 DX. The organist on the second record is Richter. See **508**.

Review:

Music/The AGO and RCCO Magazine 9/3 (March 1975): 43-44.

DE KLERK and P. KEE. *Die Orgel-Serie: Historische Orgeln*   ***342** *aus Norddeutschland,* vol. 2. Telefunken 6.35265 DX (formerly SAWT 9406/36-B [1974]). 2 LPs.

> ANONYMOUS: Nun komm der Heiden Heiland.
> BACH: Präludium und Fuge (c), S. 546.
> BÖHM: Wer nur den lieben Gott lässt walten; Präludium und Fuge (a).
> BUXTEHUDE: Auf meinen lieben Gott; Canzonetta (C); Fuga (C).
> LÜBECK: Präludium und Fuge (E).
> REINKEN: Toccata.
> SCHEIDEMANN: Jesu, wollt'st uns weisen.
> STEENWICK: Variationen über "More Palatino"; Variationen über das holländische Weihnachtslied "Heyligh saligh Bethlehem."
> WALTHER: Jesu, meine Freude.

Hendrik Niehoff organ (1551-53), St. Johannis Kirche, Lüneburg, with 18th-century additions; restored by Beckerath in 1953. Siborgh organ, Westerhusen, Ostfriesland (1643), which incorporated parts of an earlier Gothic instrument; restored by Ahrend and Brunzema, 1960. Arp Schnitger organ (1699), Ganderkesee, with pedal added by Klapmeyer (1760); restored by Führer, 1934-35 and 1948. Berend Huess organ, St. Cosmae and Damian, Stade (1669-73), enlarged by Schnitger (ca. 1688), with various subsequent revisions; restored to its 17th-c. condition by Paul Ott (1949).

Review:

Organ Yearbook 8 (1977): 95.

EUMANN. *Historische Orgeln im Rheinland.*   **343** Pelca PSR 40 573.

> ANONYMOUS: Variationen über "Wie schön leuchtet der Morgenstern."
> C. P. E. BACH: Sonata (D).
> J. S. BACH: Liebster Jesu, wir sind hier (4 settings).
> BEETHOVEN: Suite.
> BUXTEHUDE: Präludium und Fuge (f#).

Organs at Hoergsten (Thomas Weidtmann, 1732), Eckenhagen (Kleine, 1795), Füssenich (Balthasar König, ca. 1720/rebuilt by Kalscheur, 1871), Wuppertal-Beyenburg (organ case from 1693), and Radevormwald (Chr. Roetzel, 1826).

Reviews:
> *Ars organi* 25/54 (October 1977): 255-56; *Organ Yearbook* 6 (1975): 170-71.

EWERHART, SIEDEL, and TRAMNITZ, organ; HOLY and   **344**
SCHMIDT, trumpet; PENZEL and SEIFERT, horn; CASKEL,
timpani. *Kostbare Instrumente,* series 2: *Berühmte Orgeln.*
Deutsche Grammophon-Musique Royale 199 066.

Organ works:
> ANONYMOUS: Tanzsätze.
> BUXTEHUDE: Toccata (G).
> LORENTZ: Präludium.
> M. PRAETORIUS: 2 Variationen über "Nun lob mein Seel' den
>   Herren."
> SCHEIDT: Ach, du feiner Reiter.

Instrumental works:
> ANONYMOUS: Intraden Nos. 1, 5, 11, and 14 (D) for 2 organs,
>   trumpets, timpani, and horns.

Compenius organ (1612-16), Frederiksborg, Denmark; Joh. Chr. Köhler organs (1759-60) at the former Cistercian abbey of Ebrach, Oberfranken.

FEIFEL. *Die grosse Gabler-Orgel Weingarten.*   ***345**
Christophorus SCY 75110. 17-cm.

> J. S. BACH: Praeludium und Fuge (e), S. 533.
> BUXTEHUDE: Wie schön leuchtet der Morgenstern.
> HAYDN: Flötenuhrstücke, Hob. XIX:8.
> TELEMANN: Allein Gott in der Höh sei Ehr'.

Gabler organ (1737-50), Basilica of Weingarten.

FOCCROULLE. *Sweelinck und andere Orgelmeister des*   ***346**
norddeutschen Barock.
Musica Magna 50 007.

> BUXTEHUDE: Prelude and Fugue (g).

SCHEIDEMANN: Da Jesus an dem Kreuze stund.
SCHEIDT: Christ lag in Todesbanden.
SWEELINCK: Est-ce Mars; Fantasia cromatica; Fantasia No. 12; Ich
ruf zu dir.

Kern organ, St. Maximin, Thionville.

Review:

Musik und Kirche 46/2 (March-April 1976): 89-90.

FORER. *Fünf Jahrhunderte Orgelmeister der Wiener Hofmusik-*   **347**
kapelle. See **46**.

GIFFORD. *Organ Music of the Bach Family.*   **348**
Vista VPS 1088.

C. P. E. BACH: Fantasia and Fugue (c); Sonata II.
JOH. MICHAEL BACH: Wenn wir in höchsten Nöten sein.
J. S. BACH: Kyrie Gott heiliger Geist, S. 671; Nun komm, der Heiden
Heiland, S. 659; Prelude and Fugue (E♭), S. 552.
W. F. BACH: Fugue (B♭); Wir Christenleut han jetzund Freud'.

St. Mary's Church, Little Walsingham.

GILBERT. *Baroque Organ Masters.*   ***349**
Orion ORS 74155 (also Pirouette JA 19034 and Saga 5403).

BÖHM: Ach wie nichtig; Prelude and Fugue (d).
BUXTEHUDE: Prelude, Fugue, and Ciacona (C); Ciacona (e).
WALTHER: Concerto del Sigr. Torelli; Jesu meine Freude.

Casavant organ, Seminary of St. Jean-Joliette, Quebec.

GILLEN.   ***350**
New Irish Recording 003.

BUXTEHUDE: Ach Herr, mich armen Sünder; Der Tag, der ist so
freudenreich; Fugue alla gigue (C); Komm, heiliger Geist; Nun
komm, der Heiden Heiland; Prelude, Fugue, and Chaconne (C);
Puer natus in Bethlehem; Toccata and Fugue (F).
WALTHER: Concerto; Nun lob, mein Seel'; Schafe in mir.

Trinity College, Dublin.

GÖTTSCHE. *Alte Orgeln der Pfalz.*   ***351**
Pelca PSR 40566.

> BACH: Passacaglia.
> BUXTEHUDE: Nun lob, mein Seel', den Herrn.
> KOTTER: Aus tiefer Not.
> MOZART: Fantasia (f), K. 608.
> GEORG MUFFAT: Toccata (c).
> SCHREM: Sancta Maria, bitt für uns.

Historic organs in the part of the Rheinland known as the Pfalz: Stumm
organs in Mühlheim (1738), Kirchheimbolanden (1746), and Mutterstadt
(1786), plus organs at Klingen and Godramstein.

Review:
> *Organ Yearbook* 5 (1974): 143.

GROSS, organ; KANTOREI ST. KATHARINEN. *Geistliche Musik*   **352**
in der St. Katharinen-Kirche zu Braunschweig.
Pelca PSR 40514.

Organ works:
> BACH: Sonata IV; Vor deinen Thron, S. 668; Erbarm dich mein, o
>   Herre Gott, S. 721; Nun freut euch, lieben Christen g'mein, S. 734.
> BUXTEHUDE: Erhalt uns Herr, bei deinem Wort.
> PURCELL: Chaconne (F).
> WALTHER: Concerto del Sigr. Meck (b).

Choral works by:
> SCHEIN.

Fritsche organ (1621-23), rebuilt by O. Dutkowski (1951-55), restored by
Schmidt and Thiemann (1965).

GUENTHERT. *Alte Musik gespielt auf Barockorgeln der*   **353**
Steiermark.
Amadeo AVRS 5054.

> FROBERGER: Ricercar (e).
> FUX: Sonata.
> KERLL: Canzona (g).
> GEORG MUFFAT: Fuga pastorella; Passacaglia (g); Toccata
>   duodecima.
> MURSCHHAUSER: Aria pastoralis variata.
> PACHELBEL: Praeludium und Fuge (d).

7 historic organs in the Steiermark province (Austria): a 17th-c. organ by an unknown builder in the village church of Adriach; organ by an unknown builder (ca. 1750), Pfarrkirche, Ehrenhausen; Franz Mittereiter organ (1718) in the former Stiftskirche at Göss; organ by an unknown builder, Pfarrkirche, Kammern; choir organs by Joseph Geo. Schnepfleitner (1758) in the Wallfahrtskirche, Mariazell; Jos. Meyenberg organ (1659), Pfarrkirche, Murau; Andreas Schwarz organ (1722), Pfarrkirche at St. Erhard.

HAHN. *Zwei Orgeln im Hohenlohsichen Land:* I) *Bach in*   **354**
Spielbach; II) *Orgelmusik in St. Kilian-Schillingsfürst.*
Pelca PSR 40 584.

> BACH: Präludium und Fuge (e), S. 548; Nun komm, der Heiden Heiland, S. 599; Vom Himmel hoch, S. 606; Gelobet seist du, Jesu Christ, S. 614; Das alte Jahr vergangen ist, S. 604; Pastorale.
> LÜBECK: Präludium und Fuge (E).
> STANLEY: Voluntary VI.
> WALTHER: Jesu, meine Freude.

Two instruments by Konrad Koch: Spielbach, 1971-73, and Schillingsfürst, 1972. The latter instrument was built inside a pre-existent Baroque case.
Review:
> *Musik und Kirche* 45/3 (May-June 1975): 139.

HAMM. *Die Orgel in Jahrhunderten und ihre Stilepochen:*   ***355**
Der süddeutsche Barock.
Pelca PSR 40522.

> BACH: Präludium und Fuge.
> FISCHER: 3 Ricercari.
> FROBERGER: Fantasia (a).
> KERLL: Magnificat.
> KOLB: Präludien II and III.
> GEORG MUFFAT: Toccata prima.
> SICHER: Resonet in laudibus.

An explanation of the organ stops by Walter Supper accompanies these works. Gabler organ (1737-50), Basilica of Weingarten.
Review:
> *Organ Yearbook* 2 (1971): 109.

HANSEN. *Masterworks for Organ,* vols. 1, 2 — *North German*   ***356**
School; vol. 3 — *North German Followers of Sweelinck.*
Nonesuch H-71100/05/10 (re-issue from the Boite à Musique label). 3 LPs.

> BÖHM: Vater unser; Prelude and Fugue (C).
> BRUHNS: Preludes and Fugues (G, e).
> BRUNCKHORST: Prelude and Fugue (e).
> BUXTEHUDE: Canzonetta (e); Ein feste Burg; Herr Christ der einig
> Gottes Sohn; Von Gott will ich nicht lassen (2 versions); Fugue (C);
> Magnificat (1st mode); Passacaglia (d); Preludes and Fugues (d,
> f#); Toccata (F).
> DECKER: Praeambulum.
> ERICH: Allein zu dir.
> HANFF: Auf meinen lieben Gott.
> HASSE: Praeambulum pedaliter.
> KNELLER: Prelude and Fugue (d).
> LEYDING: Prelude and Fugue (C).
> LÜBECK: Prelude and Fugue (G).
> OLTER: Canzon.
> PRAETORIUS: Te Deum laudamus.
> REINKEN: Fugue (G).
> SCHEIDEMANN: Nun bitten wir; Vater unser.
> SCHIFFERDECKER: Meine Seele.
> SCHILDT: Herr Christ der einig Gottes Sohn.
> STRUNGK: Ich hab mein Sach Gott heimgestellt.
> SWEELINCK: Praeludium pedaliter.
> TELEMANN: Christ lag in Todesbanden; Vater unser.
> TUNDER: Komm heiliger Geist, Herre Gott.
> WECKMANN: Fantasie (d).

Frobenius organ, St. Andrews, Copenhagen.

Review:
> *Organ Yearbook* 4 (1973): 135-36.

HASELBÖCK, FRANZ. *B-A-C-H dargestellt in Orgel-Präludien*   ***357**
und Fugen.
Da Camera 93 232 [1970].

> ALBRECHTSBERGER: Prelude and Fugue (g).
> C. P. E. BACH: Fugue (C).
> J. C. BACH: Fugue (F).
> J. C. F. BACH: Fughetta (C).
> J. S. BACH: Prelude and Fugue, S. 898; Fugues: S. Anh. 45, 107, 110;
> Contrapunctus alla decima.

KREBS: Fugue (Bb).

Hencke organ (1749-52), rebuilt by Hradetzky (1963-64), Herzogenburg.

HASELBÖCK, FRANZ. *Historische Orgeln in Niederösterreich.*   ***358**
Christophorus SCGLX 73813 [1974].

> EBNER: Variationen über ein Thema von Kaiser Ferdinand III.
> POGLIETTI: Toccatina per l'Introito della Messa; Ricercar sexti toni;
>   Ricercar quinti toni; Ricercar primi toni; Präludium, Cadenza e
>   Fuga.
> REUTTER: Toccata (a); Christ ist erstanden.
> RICHTER: Toccata mit Versetten (d).
> TECHELMANN: Ricercar (a); Toccata (a).

J. G. Freund organ (ca. 1636-42), Klosterneuburg; Egedacher organ (1728-32), Stiftskirche, Zwettl; Henke organ (1749-52), Stiftskirche, Herzogenburg; F. X. Christoph organ (1774-76), Basilica of Sonntagsberg.

HASELBÖCK, FRANZ, organ; GABLER, horn; HERTEL, oboe;   ***359**
RIESSBERGER, flute; SPINDLER, trumpet. *Musik für Orgel und
Bläser.*
Fono Schallplatten Münster 53 001.

Works for organ with one solo instrument by composers primarily from the mid-18th century:

> HERTEL: Partita III für Flöte und Orgel (d).
> HOMILIUS: Komm, heil'ger Geist, Herre Gott; O heil'ger Geist, kehr
>   bei uns ein.
> KAUFMANN: Herr Christ, der einig Gottes Sohn; Wie schön leuchtet
>   der Morgenstern.
> KREBS: Fantasia à 4 (F); Herr Jesu Christ, meines Lebens Licht; In
>   allen meinen Taten; Treuer Gott, ich muss dir klagen; Wachet auf,
>   ruft uns die Stimme.
> TAG: Nun danket alle Gott; Nun freut euch, lieben Christen g'mein.

Hencke organ (1749-52), Herzogenburg, Austria, rebuilt by Hradetzky (1964).

Review:

> *Organ Yearbook* 5 (1974): 146.

HASELBÖCK, HANS, organ; DIE ZWETTLER SÄNGER-   **360**
KNABEN, dir. HOLZHAUSER. *Musica sacra aus Stift Zwettl.*
Amadeo AVRS 6445.

> ELSBETH: Wollt ich nicht fröhlich singen.
> GALLUS: Haec dies; Pueri concinite; Repleti sunt.
> GEORG MUFFAT: Toccata undecima.
> PACHELBEL: Toccata (e); Nun komm, der Heiden Heiland; Ricercare (c); Da Jesus an dem Kreuze stund; Herr Gott, dich loben alle wir.
> SCHEIN: Vater unser.
> STADEN: Lobet den Herren.

Johann Ignaz Egedacher organ of 1732-34, with later revisions, Monastery Zwettl.

HEILLER. *L'Encyclopédie de l'orgue,* vol. 47: *L'Orgue d'Europe*   **361**
centrale.
Erato EDO 247.

> ERBACH: Canzona a 4 (del 4º tono).
> FROBERGER: Canzona V; Capriccio VI; Ricercare VI; Toccata V (da sonarsi alle levatione); Toccata XIX; Toccata XX.
> HOFHAIMER: Salve Regina.
> KERLL: Canzona III (d); Passacaglia (d).

J. G. Freund organ (1636-42), Klosterneuburg.

Review:
> *Organ Yearbook* 6 (1975): 171.

HEINTZE.   **362**
Deutsche Grammophon (Archive) Arc 3094.

> BÖHM: Praeludien und Fugen (C, a, d); Capriccio (d); Partita über "Ach wie nichtig"; Aus tiefer Not.
> BRUHNS: Praeludien und Fugen (G, e); Nun komm, der Heiden Heiland.
> LÜBECK: Praeludien und Fugen (E, F, d); Partita über "Nun lasst uns Gott dem Herren."

Johanniskirche, Lüneburg: organ by Hendrik Niehoff (1551-52) with subsequent additions and revisions, including the addition of pedal towers in the 18th century.

HEINTZE. *Orgelwerke von Krebs und Pachelbel.*   **363**
Deutsche Grammophon (Archive) 198 403.

KREBS: Toccata und Fuge (E); Fantasie sopra "Herr Jesu Christ, dich zu uns wend"; Herzlich lieb hab' ich dich, o Herr; Ich ruf zu dir, Herr Jesu Christ; Ach Gott, erhör mein Seufzen; Von Gott will ich nicht lassen.
PACHELBEL: Präludium (d); Fuge (d); Aria (e) mit 5 Variationen; Toccata (F); Ciacona (f).

G. Silbermann organ (1710-14), Cathedral of Freiberg, Saxony.

HEINTZE. *Orgelwerke von Walther und Pachelbel.*   **364**
Deutsche Grammophon (Archive) 198 404.

PACHELBEL: Fantasia (g); Meine Seele erhebt den Herren; Vom Himmel hoch; O Lamm Gottes unschuldig; Christ lag in Todesbanden; Komm Gott Schöpfer, heiliger Geist; Werde munter mein Gemüte; Toccata (c).
WALTHER: Concerto (F) nach Albinoni; Nun bitten wir den heiligen Geist; Fuge (F); Choralpartita "Jesu, meine Freude."

G. Silbermann organ (1729-30), restored by Jehmlich (1940), village church at Reinhardtsgrimma (Saxony).

HILDENBRAND. *Die alte Orgel: Klosterkirche zu St. Urban.*   ***365**
Telefunken 6.41 097 (formerly SAWT 9534-B).

BACH: Fantasia super "Komm, heiliger Geist, Herre Gott," S. 651/651a; Komm Gott Schöpfer, heiliger Geist, S. 667.
BUXTEHUDE: Ciacona (e).
HANFF: Ein feste Burg ist unser Gott; Wär Gott nicht mit uns diese Zeit; Auf meinen lieben Gott.
SCHEIDT: Jesus Christus unser Heiland.

Joseph Bossart organ (1716-21), restored by Kuhn in 1944, monastery of St. Urban.

HILDENBRAND. *Die alte Orgel: Orgeln den Klosterkirchen in*   ***366**
Muri und Rheinau.
Telefunken 6.41 090 (formerly SAWT 9526-B).

BACH: Vom Himmel hoch, da komm ich her, S. 700; Fuga sopra il Magnificat, S. 733.
FROBERGER: Fantasia (F).

KERLL: Canzona (C).
KOLB: Präludium quintum.
GEORG MUFFAT: Toccata XIIª et ultima.
PACHELBEL: Ciacona (D); Allein Gott in der Höh sei Ehr'; Was Gott
tut, das ist wohlgetan.

"Epistle" and "Gospel" organs, both by V. F. Bossart (1743-44), monastery
church of Muri (Aargau); Christian Leu organ (1713-15), monastery church
of Rheinau, near Schaffhausen.

HÖGNER. *Orgelmusik alter Meister.*   367
Abanori ABL 820 [1974].

BRUHNS: Praeludium (G).
BUXTEHUDE: Nun bitten wir; Toccata (F); Nun lob, mein Seel, den
Herren; Praeludium und Fuge (D).
GEORG MUFFAT: Toccata sexta aus dem *Apparatus musico
organisticus.*
PACHELBEL: Präludium, Fuge und Ciacona (d).

Walcker organ, St. Paul's Church, Fürth.

HOFFMANN. *Festliches Orgelkonzert in Amorbach.*   *368
Pelca PSR 40 516.

BACH: Concerti: (G), S. 592, (d), S. 596.
BÖHM: Prelude and Fugue (C).
BRUHNS: Prelude and Fugue (G).
BUXTEHUDE: Prelude and Fugue (D).
KELLNER: Was Gott tut, das ist wohlgetan.

Stumm organ (1774-83), restored by Steinmeyer in 1934-36 and again in
1968-69, Abbey Church, Amorbach.

JACOB. *Arp Schnitger-Orgeln,* series 1.   *369
EMI 1C 187-30214/15. 2 LPs.

BACH: Präludien und Fugen (d, e, g), S. 554, 555, 558.
BÖHM: Christum wir sollen loben schon; Gelobet seist du, Jesu Christ;
Präludium (F).
BUXTEHUDE: Puer natus in Bethlehem; Lobt Gott, ihr Christen
allzugleich; Nun bitten wir; Erhalt uns Herr bei deinem Wort;
Magnificat primi toni.

LÜBECK: Präludium und Fuge (E).
LÜBECK (the younger): In dulci jubilo.
J. PRAETORIUS: Praeambulum (F).
M. PRAETORIUS: A solis ortus cardine; Sinfonie (g); Alvus tumescit virginis.
SCHEIDEMANN: Nun bitten wir.
SCHEIDT: Vater unser im Himmelreich; Ein Kindelein so löbelich; Christum wir sollen loben schon; In dulci jubilo; Echo; Modus ludendi pleno organo pedaliter a 6 voci; Paduana hispania (variations 2 and 4).
SCHILDT: Praeambulum (G).
STRUNGK: Lass mich dein sein und bleiben.
SWEELINCK: Vater unser im Himmelreich; Allein zu dir, Herr Jesu Christ; Toccata (C); Paduana hispania (variations 1 and 3); Fantasia.
WECKMANN: Komm heiliger Geist.

Arp Schnitger organs: Norden (1686-88), Grasberg (1694), Nieuw-Scheemda (1695), Dedesdorf (1697-98), Uithuizen (1701), and Groningen (1692).

JACOB. *Arp Schnitger-Orgeln,* series 2. ***370**
EMI 1C 187-30655/56. 2 LPs.

BACH: Präludien und Fugen (G, C, F), S. 550, 553, 556; Komm Gott Schöpfer, heiliger Geist, S. 667; Sonata V.
BÖHM: Präludium und Fuge (C); Vater unser.
BUXTEHUDE: Präludium und Fuge (D); Nun komm der Heiden Heiland; Puer natus in Bethlehem; Auf meinen lieben Gott.
SCHEIDEMANN: Victimae paschali laudes; Kyrie dominicale; Gelobet seist du, Jesu Christ.
SCHEIDT: Nun bitten wir; Komm heiliger Geist, Herre Gott; Da Jesus an dem Kreuze stund.
SWEELINCK: Variationen über "Mein junges Leben hat ein End"; Präludium pedaliter.

Schnitger organs at Alkmaar (1725) and Zwolle (1721) completed by Arp Schnitger's sons, Johann Georg and Franz Caspar, plus instruments at Appingedam (1744) and Leens (1733) built by F. C. Schnitger's successor, A. Hinsch.

JACOB. *Die Wagnerorgel im Dom zu Brandenburg: Werner* ***371**
Jacob spielt Orgelmusik der Familie Bach.
Aeterna 826869 [1978].

C. P. E. BACH: Fuge (d).
JOH. BERNHARD BACH: Partita über "Du Friedensfürst, Herr Jesu
   Christ."
JOH. CHRISTOPH BACH: Warum betrübst du dich, mein Herz.
JOH. CHR. FRIEDRICH BACH: Präludium (e).
JOH. ERNST BACH: Fantasie und Fuge (d).
JOH. MICHAEL BACH: Wenn wir in höchsten Nöten sein.
JOH. SEBASTIAN BACH: Präludium und Fuge (d), S. 539; Passacaglia.
W. FRIEDEMANN BACH: Fuge (D); Jesu, meine Freude; Was mein
   Gott will, das g'scheh' allzeit.

Joachim Wagner organ (1732), Brandenburg Cathedral.

KÄSTNER. *Orgelprofile: Die Silbermann-Orgel der St. Georgen-*   **372**
kirche zu Rötha.
Pelca PSR 40 504 (duplicates an Aeterna release).

BÖHM: Ach wie nichtig, ach wie flüchtig.
PACHELBEL: Aria Sebaldina aus dem *Hexacordum Apollinis.*
SCHEIDT: Da Jesus an dem Kreuze stund.
SWEELINCK: Variationen über "Mein junges Leben hat ein End."
WALTHER: Partita sopra "Jesu meine Freude."

G. Silbermann organ (1718-21), restored by H. Eule in 1935, St. Georgen-
kirche, Rötha (Saxony).

Review:
   Organ Yearbook 2 (1971): 110.

KNOWLES. *Baroque Organ Music.*   ***373**
Guild GRS 7007.

BUXTEHUDE: Durch Adams Fall; Magnificat (1st Mode).
KREBS: Andante; Prelude and Fugue (C).
LÜBECK: Präludium und Fuge (E).
WALTHER: Jesu meine Freude.

Organ, Mold Parish Church, Flintshire (Wales).

Review:
   Organ Yearbook 7 (1976): 174.

KÖBLER. *Norddeutsche Orgelmeister.*   **374**
Deutsche Grammophon (Archive) 198.372 [1964].

BÖHM: Prelude and Fugue (E).
BRUHNS: Prelude (e).
BUXTEHUDE: Nun bitten wir; Komm, heiliger Geist, Herre Gott;
Passacaglia (d); Prelude and Fugue (E); Prelude and Fugue (f♯).
LÜBECK: Prelude and Fugue (E).

Stellwagen organ (1659), Marienkirche, Stralsund. Severely damaged in World War II, the instrument was reconstructed by Schuke, 1946-59.

KOOY.   ***375**
Saga 5330.

BUXTEHUDE: Erhalt uns, Herr, bei deinem Wort; Vater unser.
PACHELBEL: O Lamm Gottes unschuldig; Vom Himmel hoch; Was
Gott tut, das ist wohlgetan.
WALTHER: Herr Jesu Christ, dich zu uns wend; Lobe den Herren;
Schmücke dich, o liebe Seele.

KRAUS. *Historische Orgeln ostbayerische Donauraum.*   ***376**
Christophorus SCGLX 73871.

GRÜNBERGER: Allegro e piu assai (E♭); Orgelstücke der *Zweiten
deutschen Messe.*
HUGL: 2 Fugen ex B und ex c.
KÖNIGSPERGER: Aria secundi toni; Praeambulum und Versetten
quinti toni; Suite sexti toni aus dem *Oberpfalzer Orgelbuch;
Fingerstreit oder Klavierübung.*
GEORG MUFFAT: Toccata sexta.
GOTTLIEB MUFFAT: 2 Pastorelfugen (D, B♭).
PACHELBEL: Magnificat quarti toni.

Egedacher organ (1732), Vornbach; Putz organ (1627), Oberhausmuseum, Passau; Geo. Schmidt organ (1572), Regensburg; Brandenstein organ (1728), Weltenburg; an instrument at Peterfecking bei Saal/Donau.

Review:
Musik und Kirche 48/2 (March-April 1978): 91-92.

KRUMBACH. *Die alte Orgel: Werke der Familie Bach.*   ***377**
Telefunken 6.41 113 (formerly SAWT 9523-B).

JOHANN BERNARD BACH: Partita sopra "Du Friedensfürst";
Passacaglia.

JOH. CHRISTOPH BACH: Aus meines Herzens Grunde; Prelude and
Fugue (E♭); Wach auf, mein Herz; Warum betrübst du dich.
JOH. ERNST BACH: Fantasie und Fuge (F).
JOH. LORENZ BACH: Präludium und Fuge (D).
JOH. MICHAEL BACH: Allein Gott in der Höh sei Ehr'; Wenn wir
in höchsten Nöten sein.
JOH. SEBASTIAN BACH: Capriccio, S. 993; Wenn wir in höchsten
Nöten sein, S. Anh. 78.

H. G. Herbst organ (1728-32), Castle Church, Lahm/Itzgrund.

KRUMBACH. *Die Bach-Orgel der Schlosskirche zu Lahm.* ***378**
Psallite 6.35 273 DX. 2 LPs.

This set includes the contents of Telefunken 6.41 113 AS (see **377**),
as well as J. S. BACH: Fantasie, S. 904; Preludes and Fugues (g, C),
S. 542, 547; Toccata (d), S. 565.

For organ, see **377**.

KRUMBACH. *Das Orgelportrait: Friesische Orgelpracht,* part 1. **379**
See **146**.

KRUMBACH. *Das Orgelportrait: Friesische Orgelpracht,* part 2. ***380**
Psallite PET 69/090 786.

BRUHNS: Praeludium und Fuge (g).
LEŸDING: Von Gott will ich nicht lassen.
LÜBECK: Praeludium und Fuge (d).
J. PRAETORIUS: Te Deum.
SCHEIDEMANN: Toccata auf 2 Clav. manualiter.
SIEFFERT: Puer natus in Bethlehem.
TUNDER: Praeludium.

Joachim Rickborn organ (1651), Langwarden; Busch organ (1737-39), Jade.

KRUMBACH. *Das Orgelportrait: Friesische Orgelpracht,* part 3. ***381.**
Psallite PET 70/070 068.

C. P. E. BACH: Fantasie und Fuge (c), Wq. 119:7.

BÖHM: Partita über "Herr Jesu Christ dich zu uns wend."
BÖLSCHE: Praeambulum ex E.
MATTHESON: Fuga No. 12 (G).
TELEMANN: Trio Sonata.
WECKMANN: Magnificat im 2. Ton.

Organs in Sillenstede (Adam Berner, 1757) and Berne (1596).

KRUMBACH. *Das Orgelportrait: Johann Patroklus Möller-*   ***382**
Orgel, Marienmünster/Westfalen.
Psallite PET 63/120 669.

    HANDEL: Prelude and Fugue (f).
    STÖLZEL: Trio Sonata (Bb).
    WALTHER: Concerto del Sigr. Telemann (c); Prelude and Fugue (d).
    ZACHOW: Jesu meine Freude.

Möller organ (1736-38), restored by Feith (1921).

KRUMBACH, organ, and **MEERWEIN,** oboe. *18th Century*   ***383**
Music for Oboe and Organ.
Musical Heritage Society 3139. (Duplicates Christophorus SCGLX 75957.)

    BACH: Christe, du Lamm Gottes.
    HERTEL: Partita.
    HOMILIUS: Durch Adams Fall ist ganz verderbt.
    KAUFMANN: Ach Gott, vom Himmel sieh darein; Du, o schönes Welt
      gebäude; Herr Gott, dich loben wir.
    KREBS: O Gott du frommer Gott; Was mein Gott will, das gescheh
      allzeit; Fantasia a gusto italiano; Fantasie (f).

H. G. Herbst organ (1728-32), Castle Church, Lahm/Itzgrund.

LEHRNDORFER. *Historische Orgeln Bayern.*   ***384**
Christophorus SCGLX 75972.

    D'AQUIN: Noel étranger.
    EBERLIN: Toccata septima mit zweiteiliger Fuga.
    GRÜNBERGER: Orgelstücke zur Messe.
    MAICHELBECK: Zweite Sonate.
    PACHELBEL: Präludium (d).

Riepp organ (1757-66), Ottobeuren; Hörterich organ (1763), restored by Zeilhuber (1969), monastery church of Ettal; Martin Jäger organ (1771), restored by Sandtner (1967), monastery church, Benediktbeuern.

Review:
Organ Yearbook 2 (1971): 112-13.

LEHRNDORFER. *Musik aus bayerischen Städten: München—*   ***385**
Frauenkirche.
Musica Bavarica 0 8 02. A 7'' record.

Organ works:
    MURSCHHAUSER: Intonation; Fuga I; Toccata arpeggiata (5th mode)
    (all from the *Prototypon*).

Other works:
    ANONYMOUS (period not identified): Aufzüge (for trumpets and
    tympani).

LEHRNDORFER. *Musik aus bayerischen Städten: Parten-*   ***386**
kirchen—St. Anton.
Musica Bavarica 0 8 04. A 7'' record.

Organ works:
    MURSCHHAUSER: Fuga II from *Prototypon*.

Choral works by:
    KALTNER and OBERMÜLLER.

LEHRNDORFER. *Orgelmusik in Ottobeuren.*   ***387**
Intercord 160 811 (also listed as 29902-4K and 074-09K).

    BACH: Toccata und Fuge (d), S. 565; Kommst du nun, Jesu, S. 650;
    Nun komm, der Heiden Heiland, S. 659; Ich ruf zu dir, S. 639;
    Wer nur den lieben Gott lässt walten, S. 647; Präludium und Fuge
    (e), S. 548.
    BUXTEHUDE: Präludium und Fuge (D).

The three Ottobeuren organs: two by Karl Joseph Riepp (1757-66), one by Steinmeyer (1957).

LEHRNDORFER. *A Survey of the World's Greatest Organ*   ***388**
Music: Germany, vol. 2 — *South Germany.*
Vox SVBX 5317. 3 LPs.

SIDE ONE.
(Renaissance literature. See **52**).

SIDE TWO.
EBERLIN: Toccata nona und Fuge.
KAYSER: Overture from *Parthia III*.
KNECHT: Kleines Oboekonzert.
MAICHELBECK: Sonate quarta.

SIDE THREE.
HOLZNER: Canzona I.
KERLL: Passacaglia (D).
KOLB: Praeludium tertium.
MURSCHHAUSER: Finale und Fuga.
STECHER: Fuga V.

SIDE FOUR.
GRÜNBERGER: Orgelstücke zur Messe.
HIEBLER: Andante und Allegro.

SIDE FIVE.
HASSLER: Canzon (5th mode); Canzon.
KINDERMANN: Magnificat (8th mode).
JOH. KRIEGER: Toccata.
RATHGEBER: 4 Pastorellen.

SIDE SIX.
PACHELBEL: Toccata (C); Fuge (C); Was Gott tut, das ist wohlgetan;
    Ciacona (f); Wie schön leuchtet der Morgenstern.

J. C. Egedacher organ (1686), rebuilt by M. Jäger (1780), Benedictine monastery in Upper Bavaria; Paul Daum organ (1723), St. Laurentiuskirche, Meeder; a modern 3-manual instrument by Hubert Sandtner, St. Martinskirche, Jettingen.

LEHRNDORFER. *A Survey of the World's Greatest Organ*   ***389**
Music: Germany, vol. 3 — *Central Germany.*
Vox SVBX 5318. 3 LPs.

SIDE ONE.
HEINRICH BACH: Da Jesus an dem Kreuze stund.

JOHANN BERNHARD BACH: Du Friedefürst; Vom Himmel hoch.
JOH. CHRISTOPH BACH: Warum betrübst du dich, mein Herz.
JOHANN MICHAEL BACH: Wenn wir in höchsten Nöten sein.
REINKEN: Toccata (G).

SIDE TWO.

BÖHM: Prelude and Fuge (C); Wer nur den lieben Gott lässt walten.
KUHNAU: Toccata and Fugue (A).
LÜBECK: Prelude and Fugue (E).

SIDE THREE.

KAUFFMAN: Herzlich tut mich verlangen; Nun freut euch.
TELEMANN: Sonata for Two Keyboards and Pedal (D).
WALTHER: Jesu meine Freude.

SIDE FOUR.

JOH. LORENZ BACH: Fugue (D).
GRONAU: Partita über "Was Gott tut, das ist wohlgetan."
VOGLER: Jesu, Leiden Pein und Tod.
WALTHER: Concerto del Signor Taglietti.

SIDE FIVE.

C. P. E. BACH: Sonata (D).
W. FRIEDEMANN BACH: Fugue (F).
HOMILIUS: Trio (G).
KREBS: Prelude and Fugue (C).

SIDE SIX.

JOH. CHRISTOPH FRIEDRICH BACH (or CHRISTIAN BACH): Fugue
   (c).
JOH. ERNST BACH: Fantasy and Fugue (F).
KELLNER: Was Gott tut, das ist wohlgetan.
KIRNBERGER: Vom Himmel hoch.

Treutmann organ (1737), Monastery Church at Goslar-Grauhof; an organ
from 1747 by an unidentified builder, Martinikirche, Minden (restored by
Steinmann in 1965-66); the organ in the Dominikanerkirche, Landshut,
originally from 1903, but completely replaced in 1965 by G. Schmid.

LOHMANN. *Orgelkonzert aus der Inselkirche St. Nicolai auf*   ***390**
Helgoland.
Pelca PSR 40598 [1978].

BACH: 5 kleine Präludien (D, g, C, e, D), S. 925, 929, 933, 936, 941.
HUMMEL: Andante (A♭).

JOH. KRIEGER: Fantasia (d) aus der *Anmuthigen Clavier-Übung* (1699).
LÜBECK: Präludium und Fuge (E).
MENDELSSOHN: Andante mit Variationen (D).
PACHELBEL: Ciacona (f); Toccata (F); Fantasia (g).
WALTHER: Warum sollt ich mich denn grämen.
ZACHOW: Vom Himmel hoch (3 settings); Präludium und Fuge (C).

LUKAS. *Historische Orgeln Oberfranken.* ***391**
Christophorus SCGLX 73 896.

ERBACH: Canzon a 4 del quarto tono.
FRANCK: Fantasie in C, op. 16.
KINDERMANN: Magnificat 8. toni.
MUFFAT: Toccata septima (c).
MURSCHHAUSER: Toccata (F).
SCHUMANN: Skizzen No. 2 (C) and No. 4 (Db).
TAG: Andantinos (A, Bb) from *Orgelsinfonie.*

Matthias Tretzscher organ (1683/84), Friedhofskirche, Neustadt/Kulm; Joh. Andreas Hofmann revision (1804/08) of an earlier organ at the Schlosskirche, Tambach; Christoph Hofmann organ (1841), St. Georgskirche in Neustadt near Coburg. The baroque compositions were performed at Neustadt/Kulm and Tambach; works by Schumann, Tag, and Franck were played on the late Classical instrument at Neustadt near Coburg.

Review:

Musik und Kirche 50/1, 37-38.

MAURISCHAT. *Pape-Orgeldokumente,* vol. 9: *Orgel der ev.-* **392**
luther. Kirche in Hohenkirchen/Jeverland. See **54**.

MENCKE. *Orgelkonzert im Friesendom auf Pellworm.* ***393**
Pelca PSR 40 556.

BACH: Toccata, Adagio und Fuge (C), S. 564; Gelobet seist du, Jesu Christ.
BÖHM: Aus tiefer Not; Gelobet seist du, Jesu Christ.
BRUHNS: Präludium und Fuge (g).
BUXTEHUDE: Ciacona (e); Gelobet seist du, Jesu Christ.

Schnitger organ (1711) on the North Frisian island of Pellworm.

Review:

Organ Yearbook 5 (1974): 143.

MENCKE. *Orgelkonzert im Kloster Lüne.*   **393.1**
Pelca PSR 40 597.

> BACH: Chorales, S. 599, 615; Prelude and Fugue (e), S. 533; Sonata I.
> BÖHM: Jesu, du bist allzu schöne.
> SCHEIDEMANN: Toccata.

MEYERS, RÖHL, SCHNOOR, and STENDER. *Lübeck:*   ***394**
Glocken und Orgeln.
Axel Gerhard Kühl 30 204.

The bells of the four major churches of Lübeck, plus the following organ works:

> BACH: Chorales, S. 600, 604, 609, 614; Concerto, S. 592; a transcrip-
> tion from *Cantata 147*, No. 10; Prelude and Fugue (e), S. 533.
> BRUHNS: Prelude and Fugue (e).

The various organs at St. Marien, St. Jacobi, St. Agidien, and the Lübeck Cathedral.

Review:
> *Musik und Kirche* 46/3, 141-42.

MOE. *Works of Georg Böhm and Johann Pachelbel.*   ***395**
Cambridge 2514.

> BÖHM: Herr Jesu Christ, dich zu uns wend; Vater unser; Prelude,
> Fugue, and Postlude (g).
> PACHELBEL: Ciacona (f); Praeludium (d); Vom Himmel hoch.

Fisk organ, Harvard University Memorial Church.

PARODI. *Orgelmusik der Familie Bach.*   ***396**
Eco 589.

> C. P. E. BACH: Fantasie und Fuge (c).
> JOH. BERNHARD BACH: Du Friedensfürst.
> JOH. CHRISTIAN BACH: Fuge (c).
> JOH. CHRISTOPH BACH: Präludium und Fuge (Eb).
> JOH. ERNST BACH: Fantasie und Fuge (F).
> JOH. LORENZ BACH: Präludium und Fuge (D).
> JOH. MICHAEL BACH: Wenn mein Stündlein vorhanden ist.
> W. FRIEDEMANN BACH: Fuge (F).

Reinisch-Pirchner organ at Toblach (Südtirol).

POHL. *Das Orgelportrait: Die Böttger-Orgel der Liebfrauen-*   **397**
kirche zu Frankenberg/Eder.
Psallite PET 169/030 675 [1976].

> JOH. CHRISTOPH BACH: Aria Eberliniana.
> BUXTEHUDE: Präludium und Fuge (E).
> SCHEIDT: Passamezzo.

Böttger organ (1970).

Reviews:

> *Ars organi* 26/55 (February 1978): 311; *Musik und Kirche* 47/1
> (January-February 1977): 33-34.

POTMESILOVA. *German Baroque Organ Music.*   ***398**
Supraphon 111 1183.

> BACH: O Lamm Gottes, unschuldig, S. 656; Toccata and Fugue (d),
>   S. 538.
> BÖHM: Prelude and Fugue (C).
> BUXTEHUDE: Prelude and Fugue (f♯).
> TUNDER: Komm, heiliger Geist, Herre Gott.

RILLING. *A Survey of the World's Greatest Organ Music:*   ***399**
Germany, vol. 1—*North Germany.*
Vox SVBX 5316. 3 LPs.

SIDE ONE.

> SWEELINCK: Chromatic Fantasy; Echo Fantasie; Mein junges Leben
>   hat ein End'.

SIDE TWO.

> M. PRAETORIUS: Christ unser Herr zum Jordan kam.

SIDE THREE.

> SCHEIDT: Toccata; Vater unser; Modus ludendi organo pleno
>   pedaliter.

SIDE FOUR.

> DÜBEN: Praeludium ex E vel A pedaliter.
> PETER HASSE, the Elder: Praeambulum pedaliter.
> J. PRAETORIUS: Praeambulum.
> SCHEIDEMANN: Nun bitten wir den heiligen Geist; Gott sei gelobet
>   und gebenedeiet.

SCHILDT: Praeambulum.
SIEFERT: Praeludium ex clave G Ag a 3.

SIDE FIVE.

BRUHNS: Praeludium.
BUTTSTETT: Christ lag in Todesbanden.
HANFF: Auf meinen lieben Gott.
D. STRUNGK: Meine Seele erhebet den Herrn.
WECKMANN: Fantasia.

SIDE SIX.

BRUNCKHORST: Praeludium.
LEIDING: Praeludium.
TUNDER: Praeludium.
ZACHAU: Ach Gott, vom Himmel sieh' darein.

Organ not identified on the album cover.

SACHS, K.-J., and SCHRÖDER. *Musik an der Praetorius-*   **400**
Orgel der Universität Freiburg im Breisgau. See **57**.

SAORGIN. *Historische Orgeln: Schnitger-Orgel zu Steinkirchen.*   ***401**
Harmonia Mundi HMS 30 577 and HM 30 304. (Duplicated by Oryx
1753.)

BUXTEHUDE: Präludium und Fuge.
HANFF: Erbarm dich mein, o Herre Gott.
LÜBECK: Präludium und Fuge (C).
SCHEIDEMANN: Herr Christ, der einig Gottes Sohn.
SCHEIDT: Warum betrübst du dich, mein Herz.
SWEELINCK: Fantasie.

Hoyer/Schnitger organ, restored by Beckerath (1946-48), Steinkirchen.

SAORGIN. *Orgues historiques,* vol. 15: *Alkmaar.*   **402**
Musique de Tous les Temps OH 15 [1966]. A 45-rpm record accompanied by a multi-page booklet (in French) on the organ.

BUXTEHUDE: Nun komm der Heiden Heiland; Nun bitten wir; Wir
    danken dir.
SCHEIDT: Magnificat noni toni.

Franz Caspar Schnitger organ (1723-26), restored by Flentrop (1950), Laurenskerk, Alkmaar.

SAORGIN. *Orgues historiques,* vol. 9: *Steinkirchen.* **403**
Musique de Tous les Temps OH 9 [1965]. A 45-rpm record accompanied by a multi-page booklet (in French) on the organ.

ANONYMOUS: Ach Gott und Herr.
BACH: Erstanden ist der heil'ge Christ, S. 628; Nun komm, der Heiden Heiland, S. 599; Wer nur den lieben Gott lässt walten, S. 691a.
BUXTEHUDE: Jesus Christus, unser Heiland; Puer natus.
KREBS: Herr Jesus Christ, dich zu uns wend; Von Gott will ich nicht lassen.

For organ, see **401.**

SCHIPPER. *Die Erasmus-Biefeldt-Orgel zu Osterholz-Scharmbeck.* ***404**
Berliton 30 005 [1975].

BACH: Es ist das Heil uns kommen her; Präludium und Fuge (G), S. 541.
BRUHNS: Präludium und Fuge (e).
SWEELINCK: Variationen über "Mein junges Leben hat ein End'."
WALTHER: Partita über "Jesu, meine Freude."

Biefeld(t) organ (1731-34), Scharmbeck.

SCHMID. *Orgelkonzert im Münster zu Überlingen.* ***405**
Christophorus SCGLX 73 847 [1976].

BACH: Präludium und Fuge (C); *Orgelbüchlein* chorales: Herr Gott, nun schleuss den Himmel auf; Komm Gott, Schöpfer, heiliger Geist; Wenn wir in höchsten Nöten sein.
BUXTEHUDE: Jesus Christus, unser Heiland; In dulci jubilo; Präludium und Fuge (g).
ERBACH: Introitus quinti toni.
FRESCOBALDI: Toccata per l'elevazione.
KAYSER: Siciliana und Rigaudon (Bb).
KERLL: Canzona secundi toni.
PACHELBEL: Partita über "Was Gott tut, das ist wohlgetan."

The "Nikolaus-Orgel" (Mönch und Pfaff, 1968) and the "Marien-Orgel" (Joh. Philipp Seuffert, 1761) of the Überlingen Münster.

Reviews:
Ars organi 25/54 (October 1977): 255; *Musik und Kirche* 47/1 (January-February 1977): 35-36.

SCHNAUFFER. *Historische Orgeln Schwaben.*   ***406**
Christophorus SCGLX 73 873.

> ANONYMOUS: Magnificat octavi toni aus dem *Orgelbuch von St.*
>   *Ulrich und Afra.*
> BAUDREXEL: Praeambulum im 6. toni.
> LEDERER: Praeambulum, 10 Versetten und Finale (C).
> MICHAEL: Praeambulae (F, d, G, C).
> SCHNITZER: Intermezzo (a).
> SPETH: Magnificat octavi toni.

Organs at Allerheiligen, Gabelbach, Violau, Mindeltaltheim, Haunsheim,
Mönchsdeggingen, and Oberelchingen.

Review:
> *Musik und Kirche* 48/2 (March-April 1978): 91-92.

SCHNEIDER, M. *Orgelkonzert in Amorbach.*   **407**
Eurodisc 114 0337 [1975].

> BACH: Präludium und Fuge (D), S. 532.
> HANDEL: Orgelkonzert No. 10 (d), Op. 4, No. 4, arranged for organ
>   solo.
> MOZART: Adagio und Allegro für eine Orgelwalze, K. 594.
> PACHELBEL: Toccata (F).

Stumm organ (1774-82), restored by Steinmeyer (1934-36).

SCHNEIDER, M. G. *Orgelmusik des Barock.*   **408**
Da Camera 99004 [1974].

> BACH: Fantasie (G).
> FROBERGER: Toccata.
> HANFF: Erbarm dich mein, o Herre Gott.
> PACHELBEL: 6 Magnificat-Fugen; Fantasia (g).

Silbermann organ, Meisenheim.

SCHÖNSTEDT. *Arno Schönstedt an der Marcussen-Orgel im*   ***409**
Meldorfer Dom.
Calig 30 460.

> BACH: Passacaglia.

BRUHNS: Praeludium und Fuge (G).
BUXTEHUDE: Praeludium und Fuge (e).

Marcussen organ (1977), Cathedral of Meldorf.

Reviews:

Ars organi 27/59 (June 1979): 554; ibid., 27/60 (September 1979): 602.

SCHÖNSTEDT. *Geistliche Orgelmusik des 17. Jahrhunderts.*   ***410**
Calig 30 441.

BACH: Nun danket alle Gott, S. 657; Präludium und Fuge (b), S. 544.
BÖHM: Nun bitten wir; Christ lag in Todesbanden.
BUXTEHUDE: Präludium und Fuge (f#).
LÜBECK: Präludium und Fuge (E).

Marcussen organ (1974), St Simeonis, Minden.

Review:

Ars organi 27/60 (September 1979): 602.

SCHUBA. *Norddeutsche Orgelmeister.*   ***411**
Christophorus SCGLX 75937.

BÖHM: Christ lag in Todesbanden; Allein Gott in der Höh sei Ehr'.
BRUHNS: Präludium und Fuge (c).
BUXTEHUDE: Canzonetta (C); Wie schön leuchtet der Morgenstern;
    Toccata und Fuge (F).
KUHNAU: Toccata und Fuge (A).
LÜBECK: Präludium und Fuge (E).
WECKMANN: Canzon (C).

Klais organ, Mittelzell Münster, Reichenau.

SCHWARB and ZEHNDER. *Die drei Orgeln der Klosterkirche*   **412**
Muri.
Pelca PSR 40574.

BACH: Chorales, S. 600, 601, 606, 614, 617-619, 625, 631, 633, 636,
    727.
FISCHER: Ave Maria klare; Christ ist erstanden; Da Jesus an dem
    Kreuze stund; Der Tag der ist so freudenreich; Preludes and Fugues
    (C, D, e, G, Bb).

Organs by Viktor Ferdinand Bossart (1734), restored by Metzler (1961-65).
Review:
    Organ Yearbook 10 (1979): 180.

SODDEMANN. *Orgelmusik in Corvey.*   ***413**
Christophorus SCS 75 136. 17-cm. LP.

 BACH: Wachet auf, S. 645.
 PACHELBEL: Toccata (e); Vom Himmel hoch.
 WALTHER: Lobe den Herren.

Organ of the former monastery church of Corvey.

STADTMÜLLER. *Die Orgelbauerfamilie Stumm in Mainzer*   **414**
Raum.
Pelca PSR 40 567.

 BACH: Allein Gott in der Höh sei Ehr' (3 settings), S. 711, 715, 717.
 BRUHNS: Nun komm der Heiden Heiland.
 MENDELSSOHN: Prelude and Fugue (c), Op. 37, No. 1.
 GEORG MUFFAT: Toccata VI (F).
 GOTTLIEB MUFFAT: Toccata.
 PACHELBEL: Ach, was soll ich Sünder machen.

Four Stumm organs in the vicinity of Mainz: Meisenheim, Flomborn, Kirchheimbolanden, Soberheim, all from the period 1740-85.

Reviews:
 Ars organi 25/52 (February 1977): 122; *Organ Yearbook* 8 (1979):
 97-98.

STOFFERS. *Choralbearbeitungen des Barock.*   **414.1**
Pelca PSR 40 583.

 BACH: Chorales, S. 676, 735.
 HANFF: 6 Chorales.
 PACHELBEL: Was Gott tut, das ist wohlgetan.
 WALTHER: Jesu, meine Freude.

SYRÉ. *Sternstunden barocker Orgelmusik.*   ***415**
Motette-Ursina 1 005.

BRUHNS: Toccaten (e, e, G).
HANFF: Ach Gott, vom Himmel sieh darein; Ein feste Burg; Erbarm
   dich mein.

Kreuzbergkirche, Bonn.

Review:

Musik und Kirche 48/2 (March-April 1978): 91-92.

TACHEZI. *Die alte Orgel: Grosse Festorgel der Stiftsbasilika im*   **416**
Chorherrenstift Klosterneuburg bei Wien.
Telefunken SAWT 9520-B [1968].

FROBERGER: Ricercar (g); Capriccio (G).
FISCHER: Präludium und Fuge (C).
KERLL: Canzona (d).
GEORG MUFFAT: Nova Cyclopeias Harmonica (C).
MURSCHHAUSER: Praeambulum, Fugae, Finale tertii toni (a).
PACHELBEL: Toccata (e); Nun komm, der Heiden Heiland.
SPETH: Toccata quinta (C).

Scherer organ (ca. 1550), enlarged by J. G. Freund (1636-42), restored by
Rieger and Kuhn.

Review:

Organ Yearbook 7 (1976): 175.

TACHEZI. *Die alte Orgel: Orgel der Franziskanerkirche in*   **417**
Wien; Orgel der Stiftskirche im Augustiner Chorherrenstift Herzogen-
burg.
Telefunken SAWT 9527-B [1969].

FISCHER: Präludium und Fuge (d).
FROBERGER: Canzona (F); Capriccio (C).
KERLL: Canzona (g).
JOH. KRIEGER: Toccata (D); Präludium und Ricercar (a); Fantasie
   (d).
JOH. PHILIPP KRIEGER: Toccata und Fuge (a).
PACHELBEL: Alle Menschen müssen sterben; Ein feste Burg ist unser
   Gott.
SPETH: Toccata quarta (e).

Johannes Woeckerl organ (1642), Franziskanerkirche, Vienna; Henke organ
(1749-52), restored by Hradetzky (1964), Monastery at Herzogenburg.

Review:

Organ Yearbook 7 (1976): 175.

TACHEZI. *Historische Orgeln aus Österreich.*   ***418**
Telefunken 6.35 066. 2 LPs.

This record set appears to be a composite reissue of **416** and **417**.

TILLMANNS. *Buxtehude und seine Schüler.*   ***419**
Calig 30 429 [1974].

> BRUHNS: Präludium und Fuge (e).
> BUXTEHUDE: Passacaglia (d); Nun bitten wir; Präludium und Fuge
>   (g); Ciacona (e).
> LÜBECK: Präludium und Fuge (E).

Marcussen organ, Cathedral of Lübeck.

TILLMANNS. *Pape-Orgeldokumente,* vol. 14: *Gloger-Orgel in*   ***420**
Cadenberge.
Fono Schallplatten Münster 63 714.

> BACH: Fantasie und Fuge (c), S. 562.
> BÖHM: Ach wie nichtig, ach wie flüchtig.
> BUXTEHUDE: Präludium und Fuge (d).
> PACHELBEL: Ciacona (f).

TRAMNITZ. *Orgelmusik der Schütz-Zeit.*   **421**
Deutsche Grammophon (Archive) 198 350 and Arc 3250 [1962, '64].

> ANONYMOUS: Tanzsätze.
> BUXTEHUDE: Ciacona (e); Toccata (G).
> LORENTZ: Präludium.
> PRAETORIUS: 2 Variationen über "Nun lob mein Seel den Herren."
> RITTER: Sonatina (d).
> SCHEIDEMANN: In dich hab' ich gehoffet, Herr; Nun bitten wir den
>   heiligen Geist.
> SCHEIDT: Allein Gott in der Höh sei Ehr'; Ach du feiner Reiter.
> WECKMANN: Fantasia ex d.

Compenius organ (1612-16), Frederiksborg castle, Hilleröd, Denmark; Fritz-
sche organ (early 17th c.), rebuilt by Schuke (1960), Kirche Beatae Mariae
Virginis, Wolfenbüttel.

TRIEBEL. *Historische Orgeln Steiermark.*   ***422**
Christophorus SCGLX 73775.

> EBERLIN: Toccata quarta und Fuge.
> ERBACH: Canzon del 12o tono a 4; Canzon (C); Canzona del 4o tono;
>   Kyrie versetten.
> FISCHER: Praeludium quartium.
> FROBERGER: Toccata (G).
> GEORG MUFFAT: Toccata octava.
> PADOVANO: Ricercar del 6o tono alla terza per organo.
> SENFL: Praeambulum 6 vocum.

Four organs from the Steiermark (Austria): Adriach (organ by an unknown
builder from the latter half of the 17th century); St. Erhard (organ by Andreas and Franz Schwarz, 1722-ca. 1780); Birkfeld (organ by Ferdinand
Schwarz, 1765); Trofaiach (organ by an unknown 18th-c. builder).

Review:

> *Organ Yearbook* 6 (1975): 173.

TRIQUE. *Les Précurseurs de Bach.*   **423**
Productions Kausmaus JPV 0.404.

> BÖHM: Vater unser; Prelude and Fugue (C).
> BUXTEHUDE: Ach Herr, mich armen Sünder; Ein feste Burg; Prelude
>   and Fugue (f#).
> GEORG MUFFAT: Toccata septima.
> PACHELBEL: Aria Sebaldina mit Variationen; Allein Gott in der Höh
>   sei Ehr'; Fantasie (g).

Basilica of Marienthal.

WALCHA. *Orgelmeister vor Bach.*   ***424**
Deutsche Grammophon (Archive) 2723 055 (also listed as 2565 086/
089 and 2712 004) [1978]. 4 LPs.

> BÖHM: Präludien und Fugen (C, C).
> BRUHNS: Präludien und Fugen (e, e, G).
> BUXTEHUDE: Ciacona (c); Ciacona (e); Passacaglia; Präludium, Fuge
>   und Ciacona (C); Präludien und Fugen (D, d, E, e, F, f#, g).
> LÜBECK: Präludien und Fugen (d, g, E).
> PACHELBEL: Ciacona (f); O Lamm Gottes unschuldig.
> SCHEIDT: Jesus Christus, unser Heiland; Warum betrübst du dich,
>   mein Herz.

SWEELINCK: Fantasia cromatica.
TUNDER: Komm, heiliger Geist, Herre Gott.

Schnitger organ, restored by von Beckerath, at Cappel.

Review:

Musik und Kirche 48/4 (July-August 1978): 196-97.

WEINRICH. *Organ Music of the Bach Family.*   **425**
RCA LSC-2793.

C. P. E. BACH: Sonata No. 1 (D), Wq. 70; Prelude (D); Adagio (d).
JOH. BERNHARD BACH: Du Friedensfürst, Herr Jesu Christ.
JOH. CHRISTOPH BACH: Prelude and Fugue (Eb); Warum betrübst du dich, mein Herz.
JOH. MICHAEL BACH: Wenn mein Stündlein vorhanden ist.
JOH. SEBASTIAN BACH: An Wasserflüssen Babylon.
W. FRIEDEMANN BACH: Fugues (F, d).

Holtkamp organ, General Theological Seminary, New York City.

WELLMAN. *Choralpartiten des Barock: Dieter Wellmann spielt*   ***426**
an der Oberlinger-Orgel der Pauluskirche in Bad Kreuznach.
Pelca PSR 40 596.

BACH: Sei gegrüsset, Jesu gütig, S. 768.
SCHEIDT: Warum betrübst du dich, mein Herz.
WALTHER: Jesu, meine Freude.

Reviews:

Ars organi 25/52 (February 1977): 121; *Organ Yearbook* 8 (1977): 97-98; *Musik und Kirche* 46/2 (March-April 1976): 89-90.

WINTER. *Die historische Orgel: Orgel von St. Nicolai zu*   ***427**
Altenbruch.
Harmonia Mundi HM 740 (also HM 30 315 I).

BRUHNS: Präludium und Fuge (G).
BUXTEHUDE: Präludium, Fuge und Ciacona.
LÜBECK: Partita "Nun lasst uns Gott dem Herren."
SCHEIDT: Christe qui lux es et dies.
SWEELINCK: Fantasia cromatica (d).

St. Nicolai, Altenbruch: the instrument dates back to the 15th and 16th centuries, but with various subsequent additions, especially those by Joh. H. Klapmeyer, 1727-30. Restored by Eberhard Tolle, 1954-57, and later by von Beckerath, 1967.

WINTER. *Maîtres baroques d'Allemagne du nord.*   **428**
Harmonia Mundi HM 34 916.

> BÖHM: Ach wie nichtig, ach wie flüchtig; Auf meinen lieben Gott.
> BRUNCKHORST: Prelude and Fugue (E).
> KNELLER: Prelude and Fugue (D).
> LEYDING: Prelude (E♭).
> RITTER: Sonatine (D).

WINTER. *Orgues historiques,* vol. 12: *Trebel.*   **429**
Musique de Tous les Temps OH 12 [1965]. A 45-rpm record
accompanied by a multi-page booklet (in French) on the organ.

> PACHELBEL: Ciacona (d).
> WALTHER: Meinen Jesum lass ich nicht.

Joh. Georg Stein organ (1777), restored by I. Wetzel in 1934-35, Trebel.

WUNDERLICH. *Norddeutsche Orgelmeister.*   ***430**
Schwann (Musica Sacra) AMS 2586.

> LÜBECK: Ich ruf zu dir, Herr Jesu Christ.
> SCHEIDEMANN: Gott sei gelobet und gebenedeiet.
> SCHEIDT: Fantasia super "Io son ferito."
> SWEELINCK: Ich ruf zu dir, Herr Jesu Christ.
> WECKMANN: Ach, wir armen Sünder.

Arp Schnitger organ (1689-93), restored by Kemper in 1948-50 and again in 1960-61, St. Jacobi, Hamburg.

Review:
> *Organ Yearbook* 8 (1977): 94.

WUNDERLICH. *Die Orgel in Jahrhunderten und ihre Stil-*   ***431**
epochen: Der norddeutsche Barock.
Pelca PSR 40 520 [1978].

BACH: Das alte Jahr vergangen ist, S. 614; Präludium und Fuge (E♭),
   S. 552; Ich ruf zu dir, Herr Jesu Christ, S. 639.
BUXTEHUDE: Toccata und Fuge (F).
PACHELBEL: Vom Himmel hoch.
SCHLICK: Maria zart.

An explanation of the organ stops by Walter Supper accompanies the above
works. For organ, see **430**.

ZIMMERMANN-STROH. *Orgelmusik in Bad Wimpfen.*   ***432**
Audite FSM 53 184 [1976].

BACH: Komm, heiliger Geist, Herre Gott, S. 651.
BUXTEHUDE: Te Deum laudamus.
FROBERGER: Fantasia I sopra Ut, Re, Mi, Fa, Sol, La.
KERLL: Canzona III (d).
GEORG MUFFAT: Toccata decima aus dem *Apparatus musico
   organisticus* (1690).
PACHELBEL: Aria prima aus dem *Hexachordum Apollinis* (1699).
SCHEIDEMANN: Nun bitten wir den heiligen Geist.

Ehrlich organ (1975), Evangelische Stadtkirche, Bad Wimpfen.

Johann Sebastian Bach

Complete Organ Works

ALAIN.   ***433**
Erato STU 71341, 71346, 71351, 71356, 71361 [1980]. 21 LPs.

Busch/Marcussen, Castle Chapel, Augustenborg, Denmark; Marcussen
organ, St. Nicholas, Kolding, Denmark; Metzler organ, Abbey Church of
Mariastein, Switzerland; Schwenkedel organ, Collégiale Saint-Donat, France.

ALAIN.   ***434**
Musical Heritage Society 534, 550, 551, 591, 599, 600, 626, 631, 633,
643, 668/70, 723, 724, 739, 747/48, 776/77, 824/25, 896, 903, 914.
25 LPs. (Reissue of Erato MCA 1 [1960-67], 25 LPs.)

Frobenius organ, Middelfart, Denmark; Marcussen organ, Mariakirke, Hel-
singborg, Sweden; Marcussen organs in the following Danish churches: St.
Nicholas, Aabenraa; St. Paul's Aarhus; Holmenskirke, Copenhagen; Chris-
tianskirke and Mariakirke, Sönderborg; St. Jakobi, Varde.

BAKER.   ***435**
FY 944 [1979]. 19 LPs.

Four Kern organs: one at Notre-Dame des-Blancs-Manteaux, Paris; three in
the Alsatian towns of Masevaux, St-Louis, and Thionville.

CHAPUIS.   ***436**
Musical Heritage Society 3000-3019 [1974-75]. 4 volumes of 5 LPs
each. (Reissue of Valois CMB 1-4, 20 LPs; in addition to being available
as a complete 4-volume set, the Valois recordings were issued also in 10
volumes of 2 discs each as MB 841-860. Telefunken has also reissued this
set in 10 volumes as 6.35 076-6.35 085.)

Andersen organs in Our Saviour's, Copenhagen, and St. Benedict's, Ringsted,
Denmark; Beckerath organ, St. Paul's, Hamm, Westphalia; Klopmeyer organ,
St. Nicholas, Altenbruch, Lower Saxony; Schnitger organ, St. Michael's,
Zwolle.

HEINTZE and WALCHA.   ***437**
Deutsche Grammophon (Archive) 3013-3030, 3118, 3124, 3204-
3207 [1947-62]. 24 LPs.

Laurenskerk, Alkmaar; Jakobikirche, Lübeck; Schnitger organ, Cappel;
Riepp organ(s), Abbey Church, Ottobeuren.

HURFORD.   ***437.1**
Argo D120D, D138D, D150D, D177D, D207D, D226D, D227D,
D228D. 25 LPs.

KRAFT.   ***438**
Vox SVBX 5441-5446 [1964]. 6 volumes of 3 discs each.

Bielfeld organ, Wilhadikirche, Stade; Bossart organ, Convent Church of
Maria-Einsiedeln; Cahman organ, Parish Church of Leufsta Bruk; Frobenius
organ, Krist Kirke, Tønder; Gabler organ, Weingarten; Hillebrand/Hoppe
organ, Liboriuskirche, Bremervörde; Huss/Schnitger organ, Cosmae und Damian Kirche, Stade; Müller organ, Grote Kerk, Haarlem; Nyhoff/Johansen

organ, Johanniskirche, Lüneburg; Riepp organ, Ottobeuren; Scherer organ, Nikolaikirche, Mölln; Schnitger organs, Pankratiuskirche, Neuenfelde, and Ludgerikirche, Norden; A. Silbermann organ, Ebersmünster; A./J. A. Silbermann organ, Marmoutier; J. A. Silbermann organ, Cathedral of Arlesheim; Wilde organ, Nikolaikirche, Wöhrden.

ROGG.   ***439**
Voix de Son Maître C 165 14.101/20. 20 LPs.

Andersen organ, Our Saviour's Church, Copenhagen; Marcussen organ, Monastery Church, Sorø, Denmark; Metzler organs — Cathedral of St. Pierre, Geneva, Monastery Church, Muri, and Reformed Church, Netstal (all in Switzerland).

ROGG.   ***440**
Harmonia Mundi 771-778. 18 LPs.

J. A. Silbermann organ, Arlesheim.

ROGG.   ***441**
Oryx EXP 21, BACH 1002-1018. 18 LPs. (Originally a Harmonia Mundi release, earlier than **440**.)
Metzler organ, Grossmünster, Zürich.

RÜBSAM.   ***442**
Philips 6767 004 [1977]. 25 LPs.

Metzler organ, Frauenfeld, Switzerland; Marcussen organ, Cathedral of Freiburg.

WALCHA.   ***443**
Deutsche Grammophon (Archive) 2722 002/2722 003 [ca. 1969-70].
2 volumes with 8 and 7 discs respectively. (Also issued on Deutsche Grammophon 2722.014 and 2722.016.)

Schnitger organ, Laurenskerk, Alkmaar; J. A. Silbermann/Kern organ, St. Pierre-le-Jeune, Strasbourg.

NOTE: For an earlier recording, principally by Walcha, see **437**.

Chorale-Based Works: Clavierübung, *Part III*

GROSS.   ***444**
Musical Heritage Society 369/370. (Reissue of Pelca PSRK 41 001/02.)

> All *pedaliter* chorales; Prelude and Fugue in E-flat.

St. Magni Kirche, Braunschweig.

HEITMANN.   ***445**
Telefunken 6.41 977.

Chorales:

> S. 669, 675, 678, 680, 683, 685, 686, 688; Duetto S. 803; Prelude and Fugue in E-flat.

Schnitger organ, Eosander Chapel, Charlottenburg Castle.

KOOPMAN.   ***446**
Telefunken 6.35 375. [1977.] 2 LPs.

> Complete.

Riepp ("Trinity") organ, Ottobeuren.

KRUMBACH. See **558**.   **447**

MOE.   ***448**
Cambridge B 2544. [197-.] 2 LPs.

Ahrend organ (1972), University of Oregon.

NEWMAN, organ; BOSTON ARCHDIOCESAN BOYS' CHOIR,   ***449**
dir. MARIER.
Columbia M2 32497 [1973]. 2 LPs.

> Complete, except for the four duets. Chorales sung by the boys' choir.

SCHOOF.   ***450**
Motette 1 012.
Chorales:
> S. 672-675, 678, 680, 682, 684, 688; Prelude and Fugue in E flat.

Klais organ, Sankt Georg, Bensheim.

Chorale-Based Works: Kirnberger Collection

SCHÄFER.   **451**
Ariola-Eurodisc 85 196 KK.
> Kirnberger Chorale Nos. 1-3, 7, 10-20, 24-28; S. 690, 691, 691a, 694, 696-706, 709-713.

Silbermann organ, Petrikirche, Freiberg (Saxony).

Chorale-Based Works: Leipzig ("18") Chorales

CHORZEMPA.   ***452**
Philips 6700 114. 2 LPs.

HEILLER.   ***453**
Vanguard VCSA 10039/40 [1968]. 2 LPs.

HURFORD.   ***454**
Argo ZRG 843/4. 2 LPs.
Rieger organ, All Souls' Church, Washington, D.C.

Chorale-Based Works: Orgelbüchlein

CHORZEMPA.   *455
Philips 6700 115. 2 LPs.

HEILLER.   456
Vanguard VCS 10026/27. 2 LPs.
Metzler organ, Netstal.

HURFORD, organ; ALBAN SINGERS.   *457
Argo ZRG 776/7/8. 3 LPs.

Sharp organs, Wollongong Town Hall and Knox Grammar School, Australia.

ISOIR.   *458
Calliope 1.710/11. 2 LPs.

Ahrend organ, Cantate Domino Kirche, Frankfurt.

JORDAN. *Pape Orgeldokumente: Hillebrand-Orgel der United* *459
Church on the Green, New Haven.
Fono Schallplatten Münster 83 7 01. 2 LPs.

KÖBLER.   *460
Telefunken 6.35 318. 2 LPs.

Silbermann organ, Freiberg Cathedral (Saxony).

NOEHREN.   *461
Orion ORS 75200/201 [1975]. 2 LPs.

Noehren organ, First Presbyterian Church, Buffalo, New York.

RILLING, organ; CHOIR OF THE GEDÄCHTNISKIRCHE,   ***462**
STUTTGART.
Nonesuch HD 73015 [1967]. (Reissue of Bärenreiter Musicaphon 1 5 26-29.)

Chorale-Based Works: Mixed Categories
Selections from more than one Bach collection

KÖHLER.   ***463**
Da Camera 193 261.

> Canonic Variations on "Vom Himmel hoch"; Nun komm, der Heiden
> Heiland, S. 659; Partita on "Sei gegrüsset."

House organ by Oberlinger.

KRUMBACH.   **464**
Harmonia Mundi 30 835.

> Canonic Variations on "Vom Himmel hoch"; 6 Schübler Chorales;
> miscellaneous chorales S. 733, 734.

Herbst organ, Castle Church, Lahm/Itzgrund.

OTTO.   **465**
Aeterna 8 26 183/184. 2 LPs.

> Leipzig ("18") Chorales; miscellaneous chorales S. 730, 733-737.

Silbermann organ, Cathedral of Freiberg (Saxony).

REICHEL.   ***466**
Jecklin 0 513.

> 6 Schübler Chorales; *Orgelbüchlein,* S. 622, 639; Wir glauben all',
> S. 680.

WALCHA.   ***467**
Deutsche Grammophon 2533 350.

Canonic Variations on "Vom Himmel hoch"; 6 Schübler Chorales; Partita "Sei gegrüsset."

Silbermann/Kern organ, St. Pierre-le-Jeune, Strasbourg.

WALCHA.   ***468**
Deutsche Grammophon 2708 023.

Orgelbüchlein; miscellaneous chorales S. 709, 727.

Silbermann/Kern organ, St. Pierre-le-Jeune, Strasbourg.

Free Works: Art of Fugue

ALAIN.   ***469**
Musical Heritage Society 4154/55. (Reissue of Erato STU 70878/ 79 [1973] and EMI 1C 187- 30 886/87.)

Marcussen organ, Laurenskerk, Rotterdam.

GOULD. *The Art of Fugue,* vol. 1: Fugues 1-9.   ***470**
Columbia MS-6338.

Casavant organ, All Saints' Church, Kingsway, Toronto, Ontario.

HEITMANN.   ***471**
Telefunken 6.41 905.

Berlin Cathedral.

KÖHLER.   ***472**
Musical Heritage Society 367/8. 2 LPs. (Reissue of Pelca PSRK 41 003/4 and Oryx 1021/22.)

Hildebrandt organ, St. Wenceslas Church, Naumburg.

KRIGBAUM.   ***473**
Mark Levinson L.5. 4 LPs.

Beckerath organ, Dwight Chapel, Yale University.

ROGG.   ***474**
Angel S-3766. 2 LPs. (Reissue of EMI 1C 151- 04 124/25 and
Oryx BACH 1080.)

Metzler organ, Cathedral of St. Pierre, Geneva.

RÜBSAM.   ***475**
Philips 6768 038 [1976-78]. 2 LPs.

Metzler organ, Frauenfeld, Switzerland.

SCHUBA.   ***476**
Christophorus SCK 70 323. 2 LPs.

Klais organ, Mittelzell Münster, Reichenau.

WALCHA.   ***477**
Deutsche Grammophon (Archive) 2708 02. 2 LPs.

Schnitger organ, Laurenskerk, Alkmaar.

Free Works: Canons; Cantata Sinfonias

ALAIN, M.-C., and O. ALAIN. *14 Canons for Two Organs.*   ***478**
Erato STU 71.103 [1977].

Choir organ, Notre-Dame-des-Blancs-Manteaux, Paris; Schwenkedel positive
organ.

ALAIN, organ; ORCHESTRE DE CHAMBRE PAILLARD, dir.   ***479**
PAILLARD.
Erato STU 71116 [1978].

   Sinfonias from Cantatas 29, 35, 49, 146, 188.

Schwenkedel organ, Collégiale de Saint-Donat.

BIGGS, organ; GEWANDHAUS ORCHESTER, LEIPZIG, dir.   ***480**
ROITZSCH.
Columbia M34272 [1976].

> Sinfonias from Cantatas 29, 35, 49, 146, 147, 149.

Positive organ, Thomaskirche, Leipzig.

Free Works: Concertos

GIFFORD.   ***481**
Vista 1067.

> 5 Concertos, S. 592-596.

St. Mary's, Little Walsingham, Norfolk.

HEILLER.   ***482**
Bach Guild BGSA 5049 (also 70 637 and HM-35).

> 4 Concertos, S. 592-594, 596.

Marcussen organ, St. Mary's Church, Hälsingborg.

KÖHLER.   ***483**
Ariola-Eurodisc H 25 950 K.

> 4 Concertos, S. 592-594, 596.

Silbermann organ, Hofkirche, Dresden.

LABARRE.   ***484**
Musica Magna 50 015.

> 4 Concertos, S. 593-596.

Kern organ, St-Maximin, Thionville.

PARODI.   ***485**
Eco 605.

> 4 Concertos, S. 593-596.

Pirchner organ, Lagundo/Algund.

RICHTER.   ***486**
Deutsche Grammophon (Archive) 2533 170.

      6 Concertos, S. 592-597.

Silbermann organ, Arlesheim Cathedral.

ROGG.   ***487**
Seraphim S-60245.

      4 Concertos, S. 592-594, 596.

Marcussen organ, Aabenraa, Denmark.

Free Works: Fantasies, Preludes, Toccatas, Fugues, Passacaglia, Allabreve, Canzona

BENBOW.   ***488**
Phonogram 6599 368 (also Philips 6504 088).

      Preludes and Fugues (g, e), S. 542, 548; Toccatas (C, d), S. 564, 565.

Chartres Cathedral.

BIGGS. *Bach at Zwolle.*   **489**
Columbia KS 6005 (formerly KL 5262).

      Preludes and Fugues (D, c, Eb), S. 532, 549, 552.

Schnitger organ, Zwolle.

BIGGS. *Bach: Four Great Toccatas and Fugues.*   ***490**
Columbia M 32933.

      Preludes and Fugues (d, F), S. 538, 540; Toccatas (C, d), S. 564, 565.

Freiburg Münster.

BIGGS. *Bach in the Thomaskirche.*   ***491**
Columbia M 30648.

Passacaglia; Preludes and Fugues (C, G), S. 541, 547; Toccata (d), S. 565.

Schuke organ, St. Thomas Church, Leipzig.

BIGGS. *Bach Organ Favorites,* vol. 1.   ***492**
Columbia MS 6261 (formerly ML 5661).

Fugues (G, g), S. 577, 578; Passacaglia; Toccatas (C, d), S. 564, 565.

Flentrop organ, Busch-Reisinger Museum, Harvard University.

BIGGS. *Bach Organ Favorites,* vol. 6.   ***493**
Columbia M 32791.

Preludes and Fugues (d, F), S. 538, 540; Toccatas (C, d), S. 564, 565.

Flentrop organ, Busch-Reisinger Museum, Harvard University.

BIGGS. *The Best of Bach.*   ***494**
Columbia M 31840

Fugue (g), S. 578; Passacaglia; Prelude and Fugue (E♭), S. 552; Toccata (d), S. 565.

Flentrop organ, Busch-Reisinger Museum, Harvard University.

CHORZEMPA.   ***495**
Philips 6500 214.

Passacaglia; Preludes and Fugues (D, a), S. 532, 543; Toccata (d), S. 565.

Organ of 1543, restored by Flentrop (1969), Our Lady's Church, Breda.

HEILLER.   ***496**
Bach Guild 70 674.

Fantasie (G), S. 572; Passacaglia; Preludes and Fugues (A, e), S. 536, 548.

Marcussen organ, St. Mary's Church, Hälsingborg.

ISOIR.   *497
Calliope 1.701.

   Preludes and Fugues (d, F), S. 538, 540; Toccatas (C, d), S. 564, 565.

Ahrend organ, Lambertuskirche, Aurich.

ISOIR.   *498
Calliope 1.717.

   Preludes and Fugues (G, b, C, e), S. 541, 544, 545, 548.

Ahrend organ, Lambertuskirche, Aurich.

KÖBLER.   499
Aeterna 8 25 561.

   Allabreve; Fantasie (G), S. 572; Fugues (c, g), S. 575, 578; Preludes
   and Fugues (c, e, a), S. 533, 537, 543.

Silbermann organ, Grosshartmannsdorf.

KRUMBACH. *Organ Works, ca. 1708-1744.*   *500
Telefunken 6.41 218.

   Fantasie (a), S. 904; Preludes and Fugues (C, g), S. 542, 547; Toccata (d), S. 565.

Herbst organ, Castle Church, Lahm/Itzgrund.

LEHRNDORFER.   *501
Intercord 120 827.

   Fantasie (G), S. 572; Preludes and Fugues (D, d, F), S. 532, 538, 540.

Dominican Church, Landshut.

LEONHARDT.   502
Philips 6575 059.

   Preludes and Fugues (e, b, C, e), S. 533, 544, 547, 548.

Christian Müller organ, Waalse Kerk, Amsterdam.

LIPPINCOTT. *Toccatas and Fugues by Bach.* ***503**
Gothic 68005 [1980].

> Preludes and Fugues (d, F), S. 538, 540; Toccatas (C, d), S. 564, 565.

Fisk organ, House of Hope Presbyterian Church, St. Paul, Minnesota.

MARLOW. ***504**
Grosvenor 1057.

> Fugue (G), S. 577; Preludes and Fugues (A, C, G), S. 536, 541, 545;
> Toccata (C), S. 564.

Trinity College, Cambridge University.

NEWMAN. ***505**
Turnabout QTV-S 34656 [1975].

> Passacaglia; Prelude and Fugue (Eb), S. 552; Toccatas (C, d), S. 564, 565.

Henderson & Wilson organ (1974/75), Wooster School, Danbury, Connecticut.

NOWAKOWSKI. ***506**
Telefunken 6.41 942.

> Fantasie (G), S. 572; Passacaglia; Preludes and Fugues (e, b, C),
> S. 533, 544, 545; Toccata (d), S. 565.

Marcussen organ (1954), Monastery Church, Sorø, Denmark.

PARODI. ***507**
Eco 590.

> Preludes and Fugues (G, a, b), S.541, 543, 544; Toccata (d), S. 565.

Reinisch-Pirchner organ, Toblach (Southern Tyrol).

RICHTER. *Die alte Orgel: Die Arp Schnitger-Orgel der* **508**
Ludgerikirche zu Norden.
Telefunken SAWD 9915-B. (Also 6.41 142).

Fantasie (G), S. 572; Pastorale; Sonatas III and VI.

This record is available also in a 2-record set entitled *Die Orgel-Serie: Norddeutsche Arp-Schnitger-Orgeln,* 6.35054 and TK 11521/1-2. See **341.**

RICHTER.   ***509**
Decca-Teldec 6.41 568. (Also Decca 116.258.)

Passacaglia; Preludes and Fugues (g, e), S. 542, 548; Toccata (d),
S. 565.

Victoria Hall, Geneva.

ROGG. *Bach Organ Works,* vols. 1 and 2.   ***510**
Angel S-37264, S-37265. 2 LPs.

VOL. 1.
Fantasies (c, b, C, G), S. 562, 563, 570, 572; Fantasies and Fugues
(c, g), S. 537, 542.

Marcussen organ, Monastery Church, Sorø, Denmark.

VOL. 2.
Toccatas and Fugues (C, d, d), S. 538, 564, 565.

Metzler organ, Cathedral of St. Pierre, Geneva.

RÜBSAM.   ***511**
Philips 6549 950.

Preludes and Fugues (A, a, C, e), S. 536, 543, 545, 548.

Chartres Cathedral.

RÜBSAM.   ***512**
Philips 6558 005 [1978-79].

Preludes and Fugues (d, F), S. 538, 540; Toccatas (C, d), S. 564, 565.

Metzler organ, Frauenfeld, Switzerland.

RÜBSAM.   **513**
Philips 6570 118.

> Fantasie (G), S. 572; Preludes and Fugues (C, c, G, g), S. 535, 545, 549, 550; Toccata (d), S. 565.

Metzler organ, Frauenfeld, Switzerland.

WALCHA.   ***514**
Deutsche Grammophon 2535 126.

> Fantasies (c, G), S. 562, 572; Preludes and Fugues (E♭, d), S. 538, 552; Toccata (d), S. 565.

WALCHA.   ***515**
Deutsche Grammophon 198 304.

> Preludes and Fugues (d, F), S. 538, 540; Toccatas (C, d), S. 564, 565.

Schnitger organ, Laurenskerk, Alkmaar.

WALCHA.   ***516**
Deutsche Grammophon 198 305.

> Fantasies (c, G), S. 562, 572; Passacaglia; Preludes and Fugues (c, g), S. 537, 542.

Schnitger organ, Laurenskerk, Alkmaar.

WALCHA.   ***517**
Deutsche Grammophon 198 306.

> Preludes and Fugues (C, e, f, b), S. 534, 544, 547, 548.

Schnitger organ, Laurenskerk, Alkmaar.

WALCHA.   ***518**
Deutsche Grammophon 198 307.

> Preludes and Fugues (G, a, c, E♭), S. 541, 543, 546, 552.

Schnitger organ, Laurenskerk, Alkmaar.

WUNDERLICH.   *519
Cantate 610 702.

> Passacaglia; Preludes and Fugues (e, F), S. 540, 548; Toccata (d),
> S. 565.

Schnitger organ, Jakobikirche, Hamburg.

Free Works: Sonatas and Other Trios

GURTNER.   *520
Claves 0 405/06. 2 LPs.

> 6 Sonatas.

Monastery Church, Muri, Switzerland.

WACKWITZ.   *521
Berliton 30 003.

> Sonatas I-IV.

Schuke organ, Evangelische Kirche, Lietzensee.

WALCHA.   *522
Deutsche Grammophon 2533 126.

> Sonatas II-V.

WEINRICH.   *523
Westminster WMS-1014 [1966]. 3 LPs.

> 6 Sonatas; 5 Trios, S. 583-586, 1027a; Aria (F).

Vårfrukyrka, Skänninge, Sweden.

Free Works: Mixed Categories
*Sonatas with Preludes and Fugues, or Concertos with Toccatas,
Trios, etc.*

BENBOW.   524
Phonogram 6581 019.

Preludes and Fugues (b, c), S. 544, 546; Sonatas V and VI.
L'Eglise Evangélique Allemande, Paris.

BIGGS. *525
Columbia M 33975 [1975].

Concerto (d); 8 Little Preludes and Fugues.

Schnitger organs at Cappel, Dedesdorf, Ganderkesee, Lüdingworth, Neuenfeld, Norden, Stade, Steinkirchen, Zwolle.

FAGIUS. *526
Bis 063.

Passacaglia; Pastorale; Prelude and Fugue (e), S. 548; Sonata I.

Marcussen organ, Vimmerby, Sweden.

HEINTZE. *Masterworks for Organ,* vol. 11. *527
Nonesuch H-71321. (Duplicates Cantate 650 232.)

Preludes and Fugues (D, b), S. 532, 544; Sonata V; Toccata (C),
S. 564.

Schnitger organ, Ludgerikirche, Norden; Beckerath organ, Christuskirche,
Bremen.

ISOIR. *528
Calliope 1.718.

Preludes and Fugues (d, g, c, C), S. 539, 542, 546, 547; Trios (d, G),
S. 583, 1027a.

Ahrend organ, Lambertuskirche, Aurich.

KLEIN. *529
Intercord 120 807.

Preludes and Fugues (D, g), S. 532, 542; Sonata VI; Toccata (d),
S. 565.

Silbermann organ, Meisenheim.

KÖBLER.   **530**
Aeterna 8 25 966.

> Kleines harmonisches Labyrinth; Preludes and Fugues (c, e, F, G),
> S. 540, 546, 548, 550.

Silbermann organ, Ponitz.

KYNASTON.   ***531**
Classics for Pleasure 40241.

> Concerto II; Fugue (G), S. 577; Preludes and Fugues (b, F, g),
> S. 540, 542, 544.

Clifton Cathedral, Bristol.

LEHOTKA.   ***532**
Hungaraton 90 016.

> Pastorale; Preludes and Fugues (f, C), S. 534, 545; Sonata I; Toc-
> cata (d), S. 565.

St. George's Cathedral, Sopron, Hungary.

MURRAY.   ***533**
Telarc Advent 5 010.

> Concerto II, S. 593; Preludes and Fugues (D, g), S. 532, 542; Toc-
> cata (d), S. 565.

Beckerath organ, First Congregational Church, Columbus, Ohio.

NEWMAN, organ and harpsichord.   ***534**
Columbia MS 7309.

Performed on the organ:
> Fugue (g), S. 542; Prelude and Fugue (G), S. 541; Sonata I.

Performed on the harpsichord:
> Fantasy (g), S. 542; Preludes and Fugues (c, b), S. 537, 544;
> Passacaglia.

Beckerath organ, St. Michael's Church, New York City.

Review:
> *Music/The AGO and RCCO Magazine* 4/2 (February 1970): 22.

SZATHMARY.   ***535**
Sastruphon 007 055.

> Concerto II; Prelude and Fugue (D), S. 532; Toccata (C), S. 564.

Marcussen organ, Holmenskirche, Copenhagen.

WALCHA.   ***536**
Deutsche Grammophon 2533 160.

> Fugue (g), S. 578; Pastorale; Preludes and Fugues (D, g, A, G),
> S. 532, 535, 536, 550.

Silbermann/Kern organ, St. Pierre-le-Jeune, Strasbourg.

WALCHA.   ***537**
Deutsche Grammophon 2533 140.

> Allabreve; Canzona; Duets, S. 802-805; Sonatas I and VI.

WEIR.   ***538**
Argo ZK 10.

> Fantasia (G), S. 572; Passacaglia; Sonata I; Toccata (C), S. 564.

Marcussen organ, Laurenskerk, Rotterdam.

Mixed Anthologies Including Both Free and Chorale-Based Works

AKKERHUIS.   ***539**
Mirasound 7 006.

> Chorales, S. 668, 721; Passacaglia; Toccata (C), S. 564.

Marcussen organ, Kloosterkerk, The Hague.

ALBRECHT.   **540**
Aeterna 8 25 877/78. 2 LPs.

Clavierübung, Part III: *pedaliter* settings of the chorales, Prelude and
Fugue in E♭; Canonic Variations on "Vom Himmel hoch."

Silbermann organ, Cathedral of Freiberg (Saxony).

BAKER.   *541
FY 044. 4 LPs.

> *Orgelbüchlein;* Schübler Chorales; 6 Sonatas.

Kern organ, Thionville (Alsace).

BIGGS. *Bach Organ Favorites,* vols. 1-5.   *542
Columbia D3M 33724; MS 7424; M-31424.

VOLS. 1-3.
D3M 33724:

> Chorales, S. 645-650, 654; Fugues (G, g), S. 577, 578; Passacaglia;
> Pastorale; Preludes and Fugues (c, d, E♭, e, F, a), S. 533, 539, 540,
> 543, 549, 552; Toccatas (C, d), S. 564, 565. (Volumes 1-3 are also
> available individually as MS 6261, 6748, and 7108.)

VOL. 4.
MS 7424:

> Chorales, S. 659, 720, 728, 731, 734; Preludes and Fugues (D, c),
> S. 532, 546.

VOL. 5.
M-31424:

> Chorales, S. 680, 753; Fantasia (G), S. 572; Preludes and Fugues (g,
> b, C), S. 542, 544, 545.

Flentrop organ, Busch-Reisinger Museum, Harvard University.

COLLUM.   543
Aeterna 8 25 601.

> Concerto IV; Partita "O Gott, du frommer Gott"; Pastorale; Prelude
> and Fugue (g), S. 542; Toccata (d), S. 565.

Silbermann organ, Reinhardtsgrimma.

DOERR.   *544
Christophorus SCGLX 73735.

> Fantasie (c), S. 562; Partita "O Gott, du frommer Gott"; Preludes
> and Fugues (G, b), S. 541, 544.

Klais organ, Monastery Church of St. Peter, Schwarzwald.

EGER.   *545
Pelca PSRS 40 505.

> Preludes and Fugues (g, C), S. 535, 545; 6 Schübler Chorales; Trios
> (d, G), S. 583, 586.

Silbermann organ, Freiberg Cathedral.

FOCCROULLE.   *546
Musica Magna 50 012.

> Chorales, S. 706, 730, 731; Preludes and Fugues (g, b), S. 542, 544;
> Toccata (d), S. 565.

Kern organ, St-Maximin, Thionville.

GEBHARD.   *547
Axel-Gerhard-Kuhl 30 207.

> Chorales, S. 622, 647, 657, 675; Passacaglia; Toccata (d), S. 538.

Heidenreich organ, St. Michaelis, Hof.

GÖTTSCHE.   *548
Da Camera Sas 007 002.

> Preludes and Fugues (F, g), S. 540, 542; 6 Schübler Chorales.

Silbermann organ, Bouxviller (Alsace).

HEILLER.   *549
Bach Guild 70675 [1963].

Chorales, S. 730, 731; Partita "Sei gegrüsset"; Fantasia and Fugue
(g), S. 542; Toccata (d), S. 565.

Marcussen organ, St. Mary's Church, Hälsingborg.

HEILLER.   *550
Pelca PSR 40 609.

Chorale, S. 622; Partita "O Gott, du frommer Gott"; Preludes and
Fugues (f, b), S. 534, 544.

Metzler organ, Steinen.

HEUDRON. *Orgelwerke für den Gottesdienst.*   *551
Unisono Pfeifer-Koch 22 547/50.

Orgelbüchlein Chorales, S. 599, 603, 607, 611, 618, 621, 622, 625,
628-630; Leipzig Chorales, S. 651, 659, 665, 667; Kirnberger Chorale,
S. 711; Miscellaneous Chorales, S. 720, 738, 740; Fantasia (c), S. 562;
Fugue (G), S. 577; Pastorale; Preludes and Fugues (C, D, g, c, d,
G, g, b, C, c, C, e), S. 531, 532, 535, 537, 538, 541, 542, 544-548.

Organs at St. Dié.

HÖGNER.   552
Mixtur 0 815.

Chorales, S. 599, 614, 636, 638, 642, 690, 691; Preludes and Fugues
(c, c), S. 537, 546; Toccata (d), S. 565.

Walcker organ, St. Paul's Church, Fürth.

JACOB.   *553
EMI 1C 047- 29 115.

Chorales, S. 646, 651, 654, 668; Fantasia (G), S. 572; Prelude and
Fugue (G), S. 541; Toccata (d), S. 565.

Silbermann organs at Arlesheim, Ebersmünster, Ettenheinmünster, Marmoutier, and Meisenheim.

JENA. *Günter Jena spielt Bach.* 554
Calig 30 410.

> Preludes and Fugues (F, c), S. 540, 546; 6 Schübler Chorales.

Beckerath organ, St. Johannis, Würzburg.

JENA. *Günter Jena spielt Bach.* *555
Calig 30 435.

> Chorales, S. 654, 668; Prelude and Fugue (g), S. 542; Sonata I.

Steinmeyer organ, St. Michaelis, Hamburg.

KÄSTNER. 556
Aeterna 8 25 664.

> Chorale, S. 727; Partita "Sei gegrüsset"; Passacaglia; Prelude and Fugue (Eb).

Silbermann organ, Rötha.

KÖHLER and METZ. *Bach auf Silbermann-Orgeln.* *557
Ariola-Eurodisc XD 86 498 K. 2 LPs.

> Aria (F); Chorales, S. 653, 656, 714, 718, 720, 723-725, 728, 731; Concertos I-V; Partita "Christ, der du bist der helle Tag."

Organ at Helbigsdorf.

KRUMBACH. 558
Harmonia Mundi (BASF) 290 336.

> *Clavierübung,* Part III: Chorales, S. 669-676, 678, 680, 682, 686, 688; 4 Duets, S. 802-805; Prelude and Fugue in Eb, Passacaglia.

Herbst organ, Castle Church, Lahm/Itzgrund.

KÜHNER. *Heiner Kühner spielt Bach.* *559
Philips 6587 007.

Canonic Variations on "Vom Himmel hoch"; Partita "Sei gegrüsset, Jesu gütig"; Prelude and Fugue (C), S. 547.

Silbermann organ, St. Leonhard, Basel.

LAGACÉ.   *560
Arion 336. 013. 3 LPs.

Art of Fugue; Chorales, S. 653, 659; Preludes and Fugues (A, b, C, c), S. 536, 544-546.

LEONHARDT. *Bach Orgelwerke I.*   *561
Philips 6775 001. 2 LPs. (Reissued as RCA RL 30 382.)

4 Leipzig Chorales, S. 656, 658, 659, 668; Canonic Variations on "Vom Himmel hoch"; Preludes and Fugues (e, b, C, e), S. 533, 544, 547, 548.

Christian Müller organ, Waalse Kerk, Amsterdam.

LEONHARDT. *Bach Orgelwerke II.*   *562
Philips 6775 018. 2 LPs. (Reissued as RCA RL 30 428 and as Musical Heritage Society 4335/36.)

Orgelbüchlein Chorale, S. 618; 3 Leipzig Chorales, S. 663, 665, 666; Miscellaneous Chorales, S. 710, 736; Partita "Christ, der du bist der helle Tag"; Partita "O Gott, du frommer Gott"; Fantasies (c, G), S. 562, 572; Prelude and Fugue (c), S. 546; Toccata (d), S. 565.

Christian Müller organ, Waalse Kerk, Amsterdam.

LUMSDEN.   *563
Abbey 760.

Pastorale; Prelude and Fugue (b), S. 544; 6 Schübler Chorales.

Grant, Degens, and Bradbeer organ, New College, Oxford.

MOE.   *564
Cambridge 2520.

6 Schübler Chorales; Preludes and Fugues (D, b), S. 532, 544.

Fisk organ, University of Vermont.

MURRAY. *The Great Organ at Methuen.*　　　　***565**
Telarc DG 10049.

> 2 Chorales; Fantasia and Fugue (g), S. 542; Toccata and Fugue (F), S. 540; Passacaglia.

Walcker/Aeolian-Skinner organ, Methuen Music Hall, Methuen, Massachusetts.

NEWMAN. *A Bach Organ Recital.*　　　　　　***566**
Sheffield S-6.

> Chorales, S. 614, 615, 649, 655; Preludes and Fugues (E♭, e), S. 552, 548.

Beckerath organ, Trinity Evangelical Lutheran Church, Cleveland, Ohio.

NEWMAN. *The 24 Preludes and Fugues (with Selected Chorale*　***567**
Preludes).
Vox QSVBX 5479/5480 [1977]. 2 LPs.

> Chorales, S. 599, 605, 609, 610, 614, 619, 621, 690, 691, 696, 699, 703, 704, 706, 714, 724, 728, 734; Passacaglia; Preludes and Fugues (C, c, D, d, E♭, e, F, f, G, g, A, a, b), S. 531-550, 552; Toccatas (C, d), S. 564, 565.

Henderson and Wilson organ (1974/75), Wooster School, Danbury, Connecticut.

OTTO. *Hans Otto spielt Bach.*　　　　　　　***568**
Philips 6587 002.

> Chorales, S. 645, 666; Preludes and Fugues (f, G, A), S. 534, 536, 541; Sonata II.

Silbermann organ, Fraureuth.

OTTO.　　　　　　　　　　　　　　　　　**569**
Aeterna 8 25 845.

Clavierübung, Part III: *manualiter* settings of the Chorales; Fantasies (G, b), S. 563, 571; Fantasy and Fugue (a), S. 561; Fugues (c, G), S. 574, 577; Pedal Exercitium.

Silbermann organ, Schlosskapelle, Burgk (Thuringia).

PIASETZKI.   ***570**
Fontana 6540 033.

> Fantasia (C), S. 573; Partita "Ach, was soll ich Sünder machen"; Prelude (a), S. 569; Prelude and Fugue (a), S. 551; Sonata VI; Toccata (E), S. 566; Trio (g), S. 584.

Silbermann organ, Nassau (Erzgebirge).

PIERRE. *Les Grandes Oeuvres.*   ***571**
RCA RL 37.084. 4 LPs.

> Aria (F); Canzona; Chorales, S. 614, 615, 625, 639, 645, 659, 671, 684, 686, 688, 721, 727, 759 (and Chorale from Cantata 147); Fantasia (G), S. 572; Fugue (G), S. 577; Passacaglia; Preludes and Fugues (D, d, E♭, e, F, G, g), S. 532, 538, 540-542, 552; Toccatas (C, d), S. 564, 565.

POISTER.   ***572**
Desto DC-101 [1964].

> Chorales, S. 656, 658, 680; Fantasy and Fugue (g), S. 542; Passacaglia.

Holtkamp organ, Syracuse University.

RAPF. *Orgelmusik am Dom zu Linz.*   ***573**
Christophorus SCGLX 75961.

> Chorales, S. 622, 683, 727; Passacaglia; Prelude and Fugue (C), S. 547; Toccata (d), S. 565.

Marcussen organ, Cathedral of Linz.

RICHTER.   ***574**
Deutsche Grammophon 138 907.

Preludes and Fugues (D, g), S. 532, 542; Sonata II; Toccata (d), S. 538.
Marcussen organ, Joegersborg-Kirche, near Copenhagen.

RICHTER. *575
Deutsche Grammophon 139 321.

Prelude and Fugue (e), S. 548; Schübler Chorales I and VI; Sonata V.
Marcussen organ, Joegersborg-Kirche, near Copenhagen.

RICHTER. *576
Deutsche Grammophon 139 325.

Preludes and Fugues (F, a, b), S. 540, 543, 544; Schmücke dich, S. 654.
Marcussen organ, Joegersborg-Kirche, near Copenhagen.

RICHTER. *577
Telefunken 6.41 350.

Partita "Sei gegrüsset, Jesu gütig"; Toccata and Fugue (d), S. 538.
Steinmeyer organ (1957), Benedictine Abbey, Ottobeuren.

ROGG. 578
Harmonia Mundi 5087.

Preludes (G, a, C), S. 568, 569, 943; Preludes and Fugues (C, c, D, e, f, A, C, d, c, G, g, a, G, g, a), S. 531-537, 539, 541-543, 545, 549-551; Sonatas I-VI; Toccata (E), S. 566; Passacaglia.

RÜBSAM. *579
Philips 6570.069 [1978-79].

Chorales, S. 645-650, 733; Fantasia (c), S. 562; Passacaglia.
Metzler organ, Frauenfeld, Switzerland.

SANGER. *The Saga Golden Treasury of Organ Music,* vols. 10   ***580**
and 11.
Saga 5428/29.

VOL. 10.
Saga 5428:
> Fantasia (c), S. 562; Preludes and Fugues (G, A), S. 536, 541; 6
> Schübler Chorales.

VOL. 11.
Saga 5429:
> Chorales, S. 684, 688; Fugue (G), S. 577; Passacaglia; Toccatas (d,
> E), S. 565, 566.

St. Mary-at-Hill, London.

SCHÖNSTEDT. *Masterworks for Organ,* vol. 8.   ***581**
Nonesuch H-71241. (Duplicates Cantate 650 238 and Oryx 1758.)

> Canonic Variations on "Vom Himmel hoch"; Fantasia (G), S. 572;
> Pastorale; Prelude and Fugue (A), S. 536.

St. Pankratius, Neuenfelde.

STRICKER.   ***582**
Arion 36.368.

> Kirnberger Chorales, S. 691, 709; Miscellaneous Chorales, S. 727, 728,
> 731; *Orgelbüchlein* Chorales, S. 622, 639, 641; Eight Little Preludes
> and Fugues, S. 553-560.

SZATHMARY.   ***583**
Record Service Alsdorf (RCA) RL 40 775 AW.

> Chorales, S. 645-647; Fugue (g), S. 578; Passacaglia; Prelude and
> Fugue (g), S. 542; Toccata (d), S. 565.

Schnitger organ, Grote Kerk, Zwolle.

VESELA.   ***584**
Supraphon 50880.

> Passacaglia; 6 Schübler Chorales; Toccata (C), S. 564.

VOLLENWEIDER.   ***585**
Tudor 73 0 05.

> Chorales, S. 650, 729, 745; Fantasia (G), S. 572; Prelude and Fugue
> (a), S. 543; Sonata V.

Grossmünster, Zürich.

VOPPEL.   ***586**
Pelca PSR 40 586.

> Canzona; Chorales, S. 622, 715, 734; Prelude and Fugue (A), S. 536;
> Toccatas (C, d), S. 564, 565.

Salvator organ, Duisburg.

WALCHA.   ***587**
Deutsche Grammophon 2565 002.

> Chorales, S. 599-622, 700, 727, 734; Pastorale; Prelude and Fugue
> (g), S. 535; Toccata (d), S. 565.

WUNDERLICH.   ***588**
Audio Fidelity First Component Series 50083.

> Chorale, S. 650; Pastorale; Preludes and Fugues (C, g), S. 542, 547;
> Sonata VI.

Individual Composers Other Than Bach

Böhm, Georg

ALAIN. *L'Encyclopédie de l'orgue,* vols. 57, 58: *Georg Böhm.*   ***589**
Erato EDO 257/258 [1973]. 2 LPs.

> Complete works.

Andersen organ, Church of Our Lady, Nyborg, Denmark.

SCHÖNSTEDT. *590
Psallite PET 142/100 773.

Präludien und Fugen (a, C, d); Capriccio (D); Christe, der du bist
Tag und Licht; Auf meinen lieben Gott; Präludium (F); Gelobet seist
du, Jesu Christ.

Führer organ, Evangelische Kirche, Provinz Oldendorf.

Bruhns, Nicolaus
Complete Works

WINTER. *591
Musical Heritage Society 3168. (Duplicates Harmonia Mundi 34.799.)

Schnitger/Klapmeyer organ, Altenbruch, restored by E. Tolle (1954-57) and
von Beckerath (1967).

Note: The complete works of Bruhns are also included in two anthologies. See **331**
and **337**.

Buxtehude, Dietrich
Complete Works

ALAIN. *592
Musical Heritage Society 309-315. 7 LPs. (Duplicates Erato EDO
207-213: *L'Encyclopédie de l'orgue,* vols. 7-13: *L'Orgue nordique: Buxtehude,
Intégrale de l'oeuvre pour orgue* [1968].)

Marcussen organ (1960), Hälsingborg, Sweden; Frobenius organ (1960), Hel-
singør, Denmark; Beckerath organ, Møgeltønder, Denmark.

CHAPUIS. *593
Valois CMB 82. 7 LPs. (Also available individually as MB 971, 972,
and MB 1.473/477, reissued by Telefunken/Decca.)

F. C. Schnitger organ (1726), restored by Flentrop (1950), at Alkmaar; J. G. and F. C. Schnitger organ (1721), restored by Flentrop, at Zwolle; J. A. Silbermann organ (1761), restored by Metzler (1962), at Arlesheim; the organ at St. Nicolai, Altenbruch, partially from the 15th and 16th centuries, but with revisions and additions, notably by J. H. Klapmeyer (1730), restored by Tolle (1854-57) and von Beckerath (1967).

Reviews:

> *Musik und Kirche* 46/5 (September-October 1976): 243; ibid. 47/3 (May-June 1977): 141-42.

KRAFT.   *594
Vox SVBX 527/529 [1976]. 9 LPs in 3 albums. (Originally released in 1961 as VBX 27-29.)

"Totentanz organ," Marienkirche, Lübeck.

LAGACE, B. and M.   *595
Calliope 1.731/38. 8 LPs.

Beckerath organ, Immaculate Conception, Montreal.

ROGG.   *596
Voix de Son Maître 2C 165- 14.051/4 [1980]. (Reissued as EMI 1C 137 16 351/58.)

Awarded the Deutscher Schallplattenpreis 1980.

SAORGIN.   *597
Harmonia Mundi HM 7-505 [197-]. 7 LPs. Also listed individually as HMU 700, 701, 741, 942-945.

The same 4 organs as listed in **593**.

Buxtehude, Dietrich
Selected Works

BIGGS. *Buxtehude at Lüneburg.*   *598
Columbia MS 6944.

Ein feste Burg; Lobt Gott, ihr Christen, allzugleich; Vater unser; Wir danken dir, Herr Jesu Christ; Fuge (C); Partita "Auf meinen lieben Gott"; Passacaglia (d); Präludium und Fuge (g); Präludium, Fuga und Ciacona (C); Toccata und Fuge (F).

Johanniskirche, Lüneburg: organ built by Niehoff (1551-53), with pedal towers and Rückpositiv added in the 18th century, restoration by von Beckerath (1953).

DANBY.   **599**
Pye-Virtuoso TPLS 13041.

> Canzonetten (e, g); Ciacona (e); Gott der Vater wohn uns bei; Magnificat primi toni; Nun lob, mein Seel', den Herren; Präludien und Fugen (F, a); Toccata (d).

Marienkirche, Lemgo: the organ dates back to the 16th century but was frequently rebuilt, including a complete rebuilding by Klassmeyer in 1887, restored by Paul Ott in two stages (1950 and 1961).

Review:
> *Organ Yearbook* 7 (1976): 172.

HANSEN. *Masterworks for Organ*, vol. 6: *Buxtehude, Selected*   ***600**
Organ Works.
Nonesuch 71188 [1968].

> Canzonette (e); Ein feste Burg; Fuge (C); Herr Christ, der einig Gottes Sohn; Magnificat primi toni; Passacaglia (d); Präludium und Fuge (f#); Te Deum laudamus; Toccata und Fuge (F); Von Gott will ich nicht lassen.

Botzen (1686-90)/Andersen organ, Vor Frelsers Kirke, Copenhagen.

HEINTZE. *German Baroque Music. Dietrich Buxtehude: Nine*   **601**
Works for Organ.
Deutsche Grammophon (Archive) 3115.

> Canzonetta (G); Es ist das Heil; Magnificat primi toni; Mit Fried und Freud; Nun bitten wir; Toccatas (f#, F); Wie schön leuchtet der Morgenstern.

Schnitger organ (1685-87), Steinkirchen.

JANÁČEK.   *602
Christophorus SCGLX 73 823.

> Ciacona (c); Gelobet seist du, Jesu Christ; Lobt Gott, ihr Christen,
> allzugleich; Nun komm, der Heiden Heiland; Präludien und Fugen
> (D, d, f♯); Puer natus in Bethlehem; Toccata und Fuge (F).

"Buxtehude organ," restored by Frobenius (1961-62), Torrlösa, Sweden.

Review:

> *Organ Yearbook* 8 (1977): 96.

KÖBLER, PROST, and TRAMNITZ.   603
Musique Royale 199 033.

> Ciacona (e); Magnificat (d); Passacaglia (d); Präludien und Fugen (f♯,
> E); Toccata und Fuge (D).

KRAFT.   *604
Turnabout STV 34283.

> Eight chorale preludes; Fugue (C); Preludes and Fugues (D, g, g).

Marienkirche, Lübeck.

LAGACE, M.   *605
Titanic 11.

> Ciacona (e); Es ist das Heil uns kommen her; Ich ruf zu dir; Lobt
> Gott, ihr Christen, allzugleich; Präludien und Fugen (F, E, g); Toc-
> cata (F).

Fisk organ, Old West Church, Boston.

Review:

> *Music/The AGO and RCCO Magazine* 11/4 (April 1977): 12.

MOE.   *606
Cambridge CRS 2515.

> Ciacona (e); In dulci jubilo; Lobt Gott, ihr Christen, allzugleich; Prälu-
> dien und Fugen (C, g, d, f♯); Puer natus; Wie schön leuchtet der
> Morgenstern.

Flentrop organ, St. Mark's Cathedral, Seattle.

SAORGIN, organ; DELLER CONSORT; DELLER INSTRUMEN-   ***607**
TAL ENSEMBLE.
Harmonia Mundi JH 929.

Organ works:
> Erschienen ist der herrliche Tag; Lobt Gott, ihr Christen, allzugleich;
> Nun bitten wir den heiligen Geist; Preludes and Fugues (E, g, e).

Choral works:
> 2 cantatas.

F. C. Schnitger organ, Alkmaar.

VIDERØ.   **608**
Valois MB 701-704 [1958]. 4 LPs.

> Ach Herr, mich armen Sünder; Canzona (G); Canzonetta (e);
> Ciaconen (c, e); Magnificat primi toni; Nun bitten wir den heiligen
> Geist (2 settings); Nun freut euch, lieben Christen g'mein; Passacaglia
> (d); Präludium, Fuge und Ciacona (C); Präludien und Fugen (F, e,
> e, f#, g, D, E, a, d, G, g); Te Deum laudamus; Toccatas (F and F);
> Vater unser im Himmelreich; Wie schön leuchtet der Morgenstern.

Frobenius organ, St. John's Church, Vejle, Denmark.

Fischer, Johann Caspar Ferdinand

ISAKSEN. *Ariadne musica.*   **609**
Odeon MOAK 8.

Frobenius organ, St. Jacob's Church, Copenhagen.
See also **782.**

Froberger, Johann Jakob

HASELBÖCK, F.   ***610**
Musical Heritage Society 1859 [1974].

> Canzona V; Capriccio I; Fantasia IV; Lamento; Ricercare IV;
> Sarabande; Suite XXII; Toccatas XIX, XXIII; Variations "Auff die
> Mayerin."

Gatto organ (1768), Pfarrkirche, Weissenkirchen; Panzer organ (1719), Stiftskirche, Durnstein.

LEONHARDT, organ and harpsichord.   ***611**
Telefunken 6.41 128 (formerly SAWT 9.569B) [1970].

Organ works:
    Canzona II; Capriccio II; Fantasia III; Ricercar II; Toccata per l'eleva-
    zione XI.
Harpsichord works:
    Suites XII and XVIII; Toccatas IX and XVIII.

Christian Müller organ (1733), Waalse Kerk, Amsterdam, restored by Ahrend
and Brunzema (1963-65).

Hanff, Johann Nikolaus

The complete works of Hanff are available on an anthology recorded by
Chapuis. See **337**.

Kerll, Johann Caspar

HASELBÖCK, F.   ***612**
Musical Heritage Society 3622.

    Canzona (e); Modulatio organica; Passacaglia (d); Toccata cromatica
    con durezze e ligature.

Pflieger organ, Basilica of Maria Dreieichen.

Krebs, Johann Ludwig
Complete Works

STOCKMEIER.   ***613**
Psallite 162/200 974, 163/240 974, 178/150 975, 179/160 975, and
191/230 976. 5 LPs.

Christoph Treutmann organ (1737), Monastery Church of Grauhof near
Goslar; Breil organ (1973), St. Agatha-Kirche, Mettingen; an anonymous
organ from ca. 1880, enlarged by Rensch; Vischer organ (1730), Ev. Peter-
und Paulskirche, Mössingen near Tübingen (restored and enlarged by Rensch
in 1974); Hammer organ, Ev. Christuskirche, Hildesheim.

Krebs, Johann Ludwig
Selected Works

GOODING, D.   *614
Musical Heritage Society 1091.

> Ich ruf zu dir, Herr Jesu Christ; O Ewigkeit, du Donnerwort;
> Praeludium and Fugue (f); Toccata and Fugue (E); Trio (E♭).

E. M. Skinner organ (1927), rebuilt by Ruhland Organs (Cleveland).

SCHOONBROODT, organ and harpsichord; GIEBEL, soprano;   *615
MAYUSSE, oboe and oboe d'amore; TAILLEFER, French horn;
ROBOT, bassoon. *13 Choräle aus dem Clavierübung.*
Schwann (Musica Sacra) 2579.

> Each chorale is presented in three ways: 1) soprano solo with in-
> strumental ensemble; 2) praeambulum on the harpsichord; 3) chorale
> prelude for organ.

A modern instrument in an 18th-century case, Probsteikirche, Kornelimünster
(near Aachen).

Lübeck, Vincent
Complete Works

CHAPUIS.   *616
Musical Heritage Society 1376. (Duplicates Valois MB 827.)

St. Nikolaus Kirche, Altenbruch (Lower Saxony), organ partially from the
15th and 16th centuries, rebuilt by J. H. Klapmeyer (1727-30), restored by
Eberhard Tolle (1954-57) and von Beckerath (1967).

Reviews:
> *Music/The AGO and RCCO Magazine* 10/3 (March 1976): 13; *Organ
> Yearbook* 2 (1971): 115-16.

Muffat, Georg
Complete Works

GÖTTSCHE. *Apparatus musico-organisticus.*   *617
Da Camera 93.204 and 93.207. (Also Oryx 1761/2.) 2 LPs.

J. A. Silbermann organs at Meisenheim (1774-76) and Marmoutier (1745-46).

SAORGIN. *Apparatus musico-organisticus.* *618
Harmonia Mundi HMU 966/67. 2 LPs.
Boisselin/Isnard organ, Malaucène.

JACOBSON. *Apparatus musico-organisticus.* *619
Musical Heritage Society 3074/76. 3 LPs.
Johan Nicolas Cahman organ, Leufsta Bruk, Sweden.

Muffat, Georg
Selected Works

DELOR. *L'Encyclopédie de l'orgue,* vol. 25: *L'Orgue d'Europe* 620
centrale: Georg Muffat, Apparatus musico-organisticus.
Erato EDO 225.

> Passacaglia (g); Toccatas I, VI-IX, XI.

Silbermann organ, Eglise Sainte-Madeleine, Morzine.

Pachelbel, Johann
Complete Works

ALAIN. *L'Encyclopédie de l'orgue,* vols. 35/40: *Pachelbel:* *621
L'Oeuvre pour orgue.
Erato EDO 235/40 [1972]. 6 LPs.

Metzler organ, Baden, Switzerland; 3 Bossart organs, restored by Metzler,
Abbey Church of Muri, Switzerland.

Pachelbel, Johann
Selected Works

BETHKE. *Neithard Bethke an der Rieger-Chororgel im Ratze-* *622
burger Dom.
Axel-Gerhard-Kühl 30 201 [1974].

Christus, der ist mein Leben; Ein feste Burg ist unser Gott; Fantasie (g); Herr Jesu Christ, ich weiss gar wohl, dass ich einmal muss sterben; Ich ruf zu dir, Herr Jesu Christ; Komm, Gott Schöpfer, heiliger Geist; Magnificat im 9. Ton; Ricercar (C); Werde munter, mein Gemüte.

Rieger organ, Cathedral of Ratzeburg.

BOLLIGER. *Albert Bolliger an den Riepp-Orgeln der*   *623
Benediktiner-Abtei Ottobeuren.
Mixtur 5002/04. 3 LPs.

28 compositions by Pachelbel: 21 played on the "Trinity organ," 7 played on the "Holy Ghost organ."

Two Riepp organs (1757-66), Ottobeuren.

Review:

Music/The AGO and RCCO Magazine 12/9 (September 1978): 15-16.

GUNDLICH. *Hexachordum Apollinis.*   *624
Thorofon KG ATH 178.

HANSEN.   *625
Musical Heritage Society 1320. (Duplicates Valois MB 822 and Telefunken 6.41 267.)

Ach, was soll ich Sünder machen; Allein Gott in der Höh sei Ehr; Allein zu dir, Herr Jesu Christ; Ciacona (f); Da Jesus an dem Kreuze stund; Fantasie (g); Jesus Christus, unser Heiland; 3 Magnificat Fugues; Präludium (d); Toccata (c).

Marcussen organ, Church of Our Lady, Skänninge, Sweden.

HELLMANN.   *626
Musical Heritage Society 3532. (Duplicates Da Camera SM 93 215.)

Ciacona (f); Fantasie (a); 4 Magnificat Fugues; Ricercar (c); Toccata pastorale; Toccata and Fugue (Bb); Warum betrübst du dich, mein Herz; Werde munter, mein Gemüte; Wo Gott, der Herr, nicht bei uns hält.

Christus-Kirche, Mainz.

Review:

Music/The AGO and RCCO Magazine 12/1 (January 1978): 17.

LAGACE.   *627
Arion 38 273. (Reissued as Musical Heritage Society 4353.)

Aria Sebaldina; Ciacona (f); Christus, der ist mein Leben; Da Jesus
an dem Kreuze stund; Jesus Christus, unser Heiland; O Lamm Gottes unschuldig; Ricercar (c); Toccata (e); Vater unser; Vom Himmel
hoch; Wie schön leuchtet der Morgenstern; Wir glauben all' an einen
Gott.

Church of St. Bonaventure de Rosemont, Montreal.

LEGUAY.   *628
Hencot AJA 100.

Ciaconas (d, f); Herr Jesus Christ, ich weiss gar wohl; Fugue (e); 9
Magnificat Fugues; Ricercars (f♯, c); Vom Himmel hoch.

TILLMANNS.   *629
Christophorus SCGLX 73 862.

Ciaconas (d, f); Fantasia (g); Partita "Ach, was soll ich Sünder
machen"; Ricercars (c, f♯); Toccata and Fuge (d).

Pfarrkirche St. Jakobus, Ersdorf-Altendorf.

WINTER.   *630
Musical Heritage Society 3399. (Duplicates Harmonia Mundi 30
582 and Oryx 1755, issued under the title *Historische Orgeln: Orgel zu Trebel*.)

Ciacona (f); Fantasie (c); Partitas "Was Gott tut, das ist wohlgetan"
and "Werde munter, mein Gemüte"; Ricercar (c); Theme and Variations; Toccata (C).

J. G. Stein organ (1777), Trebel, restored by Wetzel (1934-35).

Scheidt, Samuel
Selected Works

LOHMANN.   *631
RBM Musikproduktion 3032.

Chorale variations from *Tabulatura nova:* Christ lag in Todesbanden; Gelobet seist du, Jesu Christ; Komm, Schöpfer, Geist; Wir glauben all'.

Schuke organ, Kaiser-Wilhelm-Gedächtniskirche, Berlin.

SCHNEIDER, M.   *632
Deutsche Grammophon (Archive) 3107 [1958].

Christe, qui lux es dies; Da Jesus an dem Kreuze stund; Ich ruf zu dir; Kyrie Dominicale . . . cum Gloria; Modus ludendi . . . Benedicamus a 6 voci; Modus ludendi pleno organo pedaliter a 6 voci.

"Praetorius organ," University of Freiburg.

Telemann, Georg Philipp

BOVET. *Guy Bovet aux orgues historiques de Visperterminen.*   *633
VDE-Gallo 30 102.

Fantasie (D); Trio Sonata; various chorale preludes and fugues.

Visperterminen: an unaltered 17th-century one-manual instrument in the Waldkapelle, and the Peter Josef Carlen organ in the Pfarrkirche. The latter was subsequently enlarged by the addition of a second manual and pedal (Kuhn, 1960).

Review:
   Ars organi 25/54 (October 1977): 256.

RÜBSAM.   *634
Musical Heritage Society 1857.

Ach Gott, vom Himmel sieh darein; Ach Herr mich armen Sünder; Erschienen ist der herrliche Tag; Fugues 8, 10, 13, 14, 18, 20; Gott der Vater wohn uns bei; Herr Christ der einig Gottes Sohn; Herr Jesu Christ, dich zu uns wend; Jesu meine Freude; Komm heiliger Geist; Nun freut euch; Schmücke dich; Sonata (d).

D. C. Gloger organ (1764), Nikolaikirche, Cadenberge, restored by Janke (1971).

Review:
   Organ Yearbook 7 (1976): 175.

Tunder, Franz

ALAIN. *L'Encyclopédie de l'orgue,* vol. 60: *Franz Tunder,*   ***635**
L'Oeuvre d'orgue.
Erato EDO 260 [1973].

> Auf meinen lieben Gott; Jesus Christus unser Heiland; Jesus Christus
> wahr Gottes Sohn; Herr Gott, dich loben wir; In dich hab ich gehof-
> fet, Herr; Komm, heiliger Geist, Herre Gott; Praeludia (1 in F, 3 in g).

Marcussen organ, Laurenskerk, Rotterdam.

Walther, Johann Gottfried

ALAIN. *L'Encyclopédie de l'orgue,* vols. 28 and 29: *L'Orgue*   **636**
d'Europe centrale: Walther, Les 14 Concertos transcrits pour
orgue.
Erato EDO 228/29 [1972]. 2 LPS.

Haerpfer-Erman organ, Collégiale de St-Quentin.

BIGGS. *6 Concertos after Italian Masters.*   ***637**
Columbia M 31205.

> Concerti del Sigr. Albinoni (F), del Sigr. Gentili (A), del Sigr. Meck
> (b), del Sigr. Taglietti (Bb), del Sigr. Torelli (a and d).

Silbermann organ, Cathedral of Freiberg.

Review:

> *Organ Yearbook* 5 (1974): 144.

JACKSON, N. *7 Concerti for Organ and Pedal Harpsichord.*   ***638**
Musical Heritage Society 1319. (Duplicates Oryx 1738.)

Noel Mander organ, Westminster College, Fulton, Missouri.

LEFEBVRE.   ***639**
FY 040.

> Fugues, L. 122 and 124 (C and F); Jesu, meine Freude; Preludes and
> Fugues, L. 119, 121, 123, 125 (G, C, d, A); Toccata and Fugue, L.
> 122 (C).

LOHMANN. 640
Da Camera SM 93 208.

    Concertos: L. 127, 128, 133, 134, 140 (B♭, A, b, C, a).

SCHUSTER. *Organ Concerti after Various Masters.* *641
Musical Heritage Society 3504. (Duplicates Fono Schallplatten
Münster 63 702: *Pape-Orgeldokumente,* vol. 2: *Orgel der ev. luther. Stadt-kirche in Buckeburg.*)

    Concerti del Sigr. Albinoni (F), del Sigr. Gentili (A), del Sigr. Meck
    (b), del Sigr. Taglietti (B♭), del Sigr. Torelli (d).

Emil Hammer organ (1965-66), partially modelled after a specification by
Praetorius/Compenius.

Review:
    Organ Yearbook 4 (1973): 137-38.

CHAPTER 14
ITALY

Anthologies

ALAIN and TAGLIAVINI, organg; ANDRE and LAGORCE,   ***642**
trumpet; ARMUZZI, violin; SIVIERO and GIULIANI, oboe; INSTRU-
MENTAL ENSEMBLE OF BOLOGNA, dir. GOTTI. *Grand Hours at Saint
Petronio in Bologna.*
Musical Heritage Society 1534. (Duplicates Erato STU 70218 [1964].)

Works for 2 organs:
    CANALE: La Balzana a 8.
    GUAMI: La Lucchesina a 8.
    B. PASQUINI: Sonata.

Works for various instrumental combinations by:
    ALDROVANDINI, CAZZATI, D. GABRIELI, MANFREDINI, and
    TORELLI.

"Epistle" and "Gospel" organs, San Petronio. The former was built by Lorenzo di Giacomo da Prato (1474-83); the latter was built by Malamini (1596),
with subsequent changes and additions (1641, 1798, 1812).

BERNARD. *Berühmte Orgeln Europas: Altitalienische Orgel-*   **643**
musik.
EMI 1C 063- 30 146.

    ANONYMOUS: [untitled works].
    ANTONIO: Introduzione; Praeludio; Partita; Elevazione; Aria.
    ZIPOLI: Partita (C).

Old Italian and Swiss-Italian organs in Venice, Beronico, Montecarasso, and
Brissago.

BIGGS. *Historic Organs of Italy.* See **63**.   **644**

BIGGS, organ; BOSTON BRASS ENSEMBLE, dir. BURGIN. *Music*   **645**
for Organ and Brass. See **64**.

EWERHART and SIEDEL.   **646**
Deutsche Grammophon (Archive) 198 349.

    ANONYMOUS: Intraden.
    LUCCHINETTI: Konzert für 2 Orgeln (B♭); Sonate oder Konzert für
      2 Orgeln (D).
    PIAZZA: Sonata für 2 Orgeln.
    TERRENI: Sonate für 2 Orgeln.

GERMANI. *Altitalienische Orgelmusik.*   **647**
Deutsche Grammophon (Archive) 2533 043 [1969].

    BENCINI: Fugue (G); Sonata (f).
    CASINI: Pensiero per organo II (D).
    FRESCOBALDI: Toccata prima (g); Toccata terza (D); Toccata quar-
      ta (A); Toccata quinta (G); Toccata sesta (F).
    PASQUINI: Sonata "Elevazione" (e); Toccata dell' VIIIº tono (G).
    PORPORA: Fugue (E♭).
    ZIPOLI: Canzona (g).

Nacchini organ (1751), Santa Maria del Riposo, Venice, rebuilt by Ruffatti
(1960).

HILDENBRAND. *Historische Orgeln in Brissago und Monte-*   ***648**
carasso.
Telefunken 6.41 890.

    FRESCOBALDI: Bergamasca.
    GALUPPI: Sonata.
    MERULO: Canzon a 4 dita "La Leonora."
    ROSSI: Toccata VIIª; Toccata cromatica per l'elevazione.
    TRABACI: Canzona francese settima cromatica.
    ZIPOLI: Toccata.

Italian instruments from 1696 (Brissago) and 1746 (Montecarasso) in the Italian-speaking part of Switzerland.

Review:

> *Organ Yearbook* 8 (1977): 95-96.

INNOCENTI. *Italian Organ Music.*   ***648.1**
Musical Heritage Society 4064. (Duplicates Dischi Ricordi 1013.)

> CIMA: Canzona francese.
> MAYONE: Toccata V.
> MERULA: Capriccio; Canzona IV; Sonata cromatica.
> ROSSI: Toccatas VI and XIV.
> SALVATORE: Canzona francese III; Toccata I.
> STORACE: Toccata e canzona.
> TRABACI: Durezze e ligature; Canto fermo II; Canzona francese VII.

INNOCENTI, SPINELLI, TAGLIAVINI, and ZOJA. *Euro-*   **649**
päische Orgellandschaften: Historische Orgeln in Italien. See **68.**

LITAIZE. *Les Sommets de l'orgue: Anciens Maîtres d'Espagne*   **650**
et d'Italie. See **823.**

PIERRE. *L'Orgue italien.*   **651**
RCA 650 021.

> FRESCOBALDI: Aria detta la Frescobalda; Canzon nona detta la
>   Querina; Capriccio sopra la bassa fiamenga; Toccata ottava di
>   durezze e ligature; Toccata quarta; Toccata quinta.
> A. GABRIELI: Ricercare nel duodecimo tono.
> G. GABRIELI: Canzon "La Spiritata."
> GALUPPI: Allegro; Sonate con risposta di flauto.
> A. SCARLATTI: Toccata XI.
> ZIPOLI: Pastorale e canzone (g).

Callido and Piagga organs (18th c.), Saint Mark's, Venice.

Review:

> *Music/The AGO and RCCO Magazine* 10/7 (July 1976): 12.

SAORGIN. *Orgues historiques. Le Monde de l'orgue No. 3:*   ***652**
L'Orgue de Tende.
Harmonia Mundi 947.

    DAVIDE: Sinfonia; Sonatina.
    MARTINI: 4 Sonatas "sui flauti."
    PETRALI: Fantasia concertante.
    ZIPOLI: 6 Canzone.

Serassi organ (1807).

SAORGIN. *Orgues historiques,* vol. 8: *Santa Maria, Bastia.*   **653**
Musique de Tous les Temps OH 8 [1964]. A 45-rpm record accompanied by a multi-page booklet (in French) on the organ.

    FRESCOBALDI: Iste confessor; Toccata per l'elevazione (*Messa della Madonna*).
    A. GABRIELI: Ricercare, Mode XII.
    LUZZASCHI: Toccata, Mode IV.
    MALVEZZI: Canzone.

Serassi organ (1844) in classic style, Cathedral of Santa Maria, Bastia (Corsica).

SCHUBA: *Master Organists of the 16th, 17th and 18th Centuries*   ***654**
in Italy.
Musical Heritage Society 3193. (Duplicates Christophorus SCGLX 75 930.)

    ARESTI: Pange lingua.
    BANCHIERI: Dialogo (*L'Organo suonarino*).
    G. CAVAZZONI: Veni Creator Spiritus.
    CIAJA: Ricercar (d).
    FRESCOBALDI: Canzon (F); Toccata per l'elevazione.
    MARTINI: Prelude and Fugue (C).
    POGLIETTI: Ricercar V[i] toni.
    PORPORA: Fuga (E♭).
    ROSSI: Toccata VI.
    D. SCARLATTI: Sonata fuga per organo.
    ZIPOLI: Canzona (g); Elevazione (F); Offertorio (C).

Organ from ca. 1780 by an unknown builder, Castle Church, Mainau, restored by Mühleisen in the early 1960s.

Review:
    Organ Yearbook 6 (1975): 74.

SIEDEL, organ; HOEFFLIN, tenor; KOCH, viola da gamba.   ***655**
O quam pulchra es: Italienische Marienmusik des 17. Jahrhunderts.

Organ works:

FRESCOBALDI: Toccata per l'elevazione; Toccata I (1637).
MERULA: Intonatione chromatica.
ROSSI: Toccata VII.

Vocal works by:

BERNARDI, CAPRIOLI, GRANDI, GRATIANI, MONFERRATO, and
MONTEVERDI.

TAGLIAVINI. *Italian Organ Music of the 17th and 18th*   ***656**
Centuries.
Musical Heritage Society 954. (Duplicates Erato EDO 232 and Christophorus
CGLP 835.)

FRESCOBALDI: Canzone I; Toccata col contrabasso ovvero pedale.
MERULA: Canzone (C); Capriccio cromatico; Intonazione cromatica
del 4º tono.
PASQUINI: Introduzione e pastorale.
ROSSI: Toccata III; Toccata (C).
D. SCARLATTI: Sonata (D), L. 57; Sonata (G), L. suppl. 57.
TRABACI: Canto fermo del 2º tono; Consonanze stravaganti; Toc-
cata IV.
ZIPOLI: Elevazione (F); Offertorio (C); Pastorale (C).

Serassi organ, Pisogne (a mid-19th-century instrument in classic style).

TERNI. *A Survey of the World's Greatest Organ Music: Italy,*   **657**
vol. 1: *Composers from Emilia and Lombardy.* See **75.**

TERNI. *A Survey of the World's Greatest Organ Music: Italy,*   **658**
vol. 2: *Lombard Composers and the Venetian School.* See **76.**

TERNI. *A Survey of the World's Greatest Organ Music: Italy,*   ***659**
vol. 3: *Venetian School.*
Vox SVBX 5324. 3 LPs.

SIDE ONE.
> DIRUTA: Canzone; Ricercare; 2 Toccatas.
> MERULO: Kyrie, Christe, Kyrie.
> ROMANINI: Toccata.

SIDE TWO.
> G. GABRIELI: Canzone; Fuga; Intonazione; Ricercare.

SIDE THREE.
> MARCELLO: Cantabile; 2 Fugas.
> POLLAROLI: Sonata.

SIDE FOUR.
> GALUPPI: Allegro; Largo; Sonata; Sonata per flauto.

SIDE FIVE.
> GALUPPI: Andante; Allegro; Allegro e spiritoso; Sonata.

SIDE SIX:
> GALUPPI: Andante.
> PESCETTI: Sonatas I and III.

San Domenico di Prato, Florence: a 16th-century organ with 19th-century additions.

Review:
> *Musik und Kirche* 46/3 (May-June 1976): 142-43.

ZANABONI. *Antichi organi italiani del '700.*   **660**
Vedette VST 6004.

> DELLA CIAIA: 3 Ricercari.
> MARTINI: Largo.
> B. PASQUINI: Toccata (g); 3 Arie.
> ROSSI: Toccatas (C, F).
> A. SCARLATTI: Toccata XI.
> ZIPOLI: Pastorale; Elevazione (F); Verso e Canzona (C).

Bossi organ (1797), restored by Tronci (ca. 1900), in the Roncole Verdi di Busseto (Parma); 18th-century positive by an unknown builder.

Individual Composers

Frescobaldi, Girolamo

ANTONINI.   *661
Arion 38.318.

> Aria detta la Frescobalda; Canzone I-VI; Toccatas III-V.

Doré organ, Notre-Dame-des-Doms, Avignon.

ANTONINI, organ; CAREY, baritone; ENSEMBLE VOCAL   *662
AVIGNON, dir. DURAND. *Fiori musicali* (complete).
Musical Heritage Society 1987/88. 2 LPs. (Duplicates Arion 31.915/16.)

Doré organ, Notre-Dame-des-Doms, Avignon.

DALLA LIBERA.   *663
Telefunken 6.41 913 [1974].

> Canzona quarta; Capriccio pastorale; Gagliarda III; La Frescobalda;
> Ricercare dopo il Credo; Toccatas I, II, V, VII; Toccata avanti il ricer-
> care e ricercare cromatico dopo il credo; Toccata avanti la messa della
> Domenica e tre Kyrie; Toccata cromatica per l'elevazione; Toccata
> di durezze e ligature; Toccata per l'elevazione.

Tamburini organ (20th c.), Istituto Pia Casa dei Poveri, Trieste.

Review:
> *Musik und Kirche* 46/2 (March-April 1976): 88.

HAMMOND, organ and harpsichord.   *664
Orion 73131.

> 12 toccatas from *Il secondo libro di toccate.*

Anonymous 18th-century Italian organ restored by Formentelli (1969); Berg
harpsichord (1970).

LEONHARDT. *Historische Orgeln: Orgel von Antegnati,*   665
Brescia um 1630.
Harmonia Mundi SM 30 317.

> Selected toccatas.

LEONHARDT, organ and harpisichord. *The Art of Frescobaldi.* **666**
Bach Guild-Vanguard BG 568 [1956].

> Canzona seconda; Capriccio di durezze; Cento partite sopra
> passacagli; Magnificat secundi toni; Partite "La Moniche"; Ricercar
> sopra mi, re, fa, mi; Toccata nona; Toccata per l'elevatione; Toccata
> quinta sopra i pedali; Toccata sesta sopra i pedali.

16th-century Italian organ, Silver Chapel, Hofkirche, Innsbruck; Neupert
harpsichord.

LEONHARDT, organ and harpsichord.   **667**
Harmonia Mundi HM 32 317.

> Canzona sesta; Capriccio secondo sopra la, sol, fa, mi, re, ut; Cento
> partite sopra passacagli; Fantasia sesta sopra doi soggetti; Recercar
> terzo; Toccatas VIII and IX; Toccata VI (Turin tablature); Toccata
> per l'elevatione.

Antegnati organ (1635-36), San Carlo, Brescia; Ruckers harpsichord (1640).

Review:

> *Organ Yearbook* 4 (1973): 141.

MÜLLER, organ; NEUMEYER, harpsichord. *The Italian Sei-*   **668**
cento: series C: *The Toccata.*
Deutsche Grammophon (Archive) 3054 [1956].

Organ works:

> Recercare post il Credo (*Messa delli Apostoli*); Toccata cromaticha
> per l'elevazione (*Messa della Domenica*); Toccata per l'elevazione
> (*Messa della Madonna*); Toccatas V & VI (*Il secondo libro di toccate*
> . . .).

Harpsichord works from:

> *Toccate e Partite . . . Libro I* and *Il secondo libro.* . . .

16th-century Italian organ, Silver Chapel, Hofkirche, Innsbruck.

MOE.   **669**
Cambridge CRS 2516 [1973].

Ave maris stella (1637); Bergamasca (1635); Canzona "La Rovetta" (1645); Ricercar VII (1626); Romanesca variations (1637); Toccatas V and VII (1637); Toccata per l'elevazione (*Fiori musicali*).

Italian organ, ca. 1750, presently at the University of California, Berkeley.

ROGG.   670
Voix de Son Maître C 069- 73 038.

   Ten Toccatas.

Brescia.

ROGG.   671
Voix de Son Maître C 069- 73 039.

   Bergamasca; Canzoni alla francese.

SAORGIN. *Historische Orgeln: Serassi-Orgel zu Bastia.*   672
Harmonia Mundi HM 537 and HMS 30 537.

   Bergamasca; Canzona Iᵃ "La Rovetta"; Canzona IIIᵃ "La Crivelli";
   Canzona Vᵃ "La Bellerofonte"; Canzona VIᵃ "La Pesenti"; Canzona
   VIIᵃ "La Traditi"; Ricercare con obligo del basso; Toccatas Iᵃ, IVᵃ,
   Vᵃ per l'elevazione.

Serassi organ (1844) in classic style, Cathedral of Santa Maria, Bastia (Corsica).

SAORGIN.   673
Harmonia Mundi HMU 727. (Reissued in part on Musical Heritage Society 4014.)

   Canzon Iᵃ (1626); Canzone Iᵃ, IIᵃ, IVᵃ (1637); Canzone alla francese:
   "La Bellerofonte," "La Pesenti," "La Traditi," "La Querina" (1645);
   Capriccio sopra la bassa fiamenga; Ricercar X; Toccate II, IV, XI
   (1627).

Antegnati organ, San Giuseppe, Brescia.

TAGLIAVINI. *The Organ of San Bernardino di Carpi.*   ***674**
Musical Heritage Society 3627. (Duplicates a disc in the *Antichi organi italiani* series.)

> Canzone IV and VI; Capriccio I sopra ut, re, mi, fa, sol, la; Capriccio sopra la Girolmeta; Toccatas III and IV da sonarsi all' elevazione; Toccata IV sopra i pedali e senza; Toccata V sopra i pedali e senza.

Organ by an anonymous 17th-century builder, San Bernardino di Carpi, Modena.

TAGLIAVINI, organ; CORO DELL' IMMACOLATA DI BRESCIA.   ***675**
Fiori musicali (complete).
Erato STU 70.918. 2 LPs (duplicates EMI 1C 187-30 897/98 [1975]).

Antegnati organ (1581), San Giuseppe, Brescia.

Review:
> *Musik und Kirche* 47/1 (January-February 1977): 34-35.

CHAPTER 15
THE LOW COUNTRIES

Anthologies

Since one or two works by Sweelinck are often included on a recording devoted other-wise to German organ music, most recordings of this type have been listed with the German anthologies.

BIGGS. *Famous Organs of Holland and Northern Germany.*   **676**
See **742**.

DE KLERK. *Die alte Orgel: Arp Schnitger-Orgeln von Stein-*   **677**
kirchen und Neuenfelde. See **341**.

DE KLERK and KEE, P. *Die Orgel-Serie: Historische Orgeln*   **678**
aus Norddeutschland, vol. 2. See **342**.

FOCCROULLE. *Sweelinck und andere Orgelmeister des nord-*   **679**
deutschen Barock. See **346**.

FROIDEBISE, A., organ; CHORALE ST. LAMBERT, VERVIERS.   ***680**
Plainsong from Liège.
Monumenta Belgicae Musicae 38.

Organ works:
> ANONYMOUS: Plein jeu (d).
> BABOU: Fantasies.
> LOHET: Canzone; Fugues 1-3.
> MONTE: Magnum triumphum.
> SCRONX: Echo.

Gregorian (Liège) chant for Corpus Christi.

HANSEN. *Masterworks for Organ,* vol. 7: *The Netherlands,*   ***681**
17th Century.
Nonesuch H-71214 [1969].

> BULL: Prelude and Carol "Laet ons met herten reijne."
> CORNET: Toccata, Tone III.
> KERCKHOVEN: Fantasia pro duplici organo.
> LUYTHON: Fuga gravissima.
> NOORDT: Psalm 6.
> SCRONX: Echo.
> SPEUY: Psalm 118.
> SWEELINCK: Echo Fantasia.

Marcussen organ, Jaegersborg, Denmark.

JACOB. *Arp Schnitger-Orgeln,* series 1. See **369.**   **682**

LEFEBVRE. *Orgue des Flandres.*   ***683**
FY 085.

> BABOU: Fantaisie des trompettes basses et hautes.
> CORNET: 5 Versets on "Salve Regina."
> KERCKHOVEN: Fugue (C); Prelude and Fugue (d).
> SWEELINCK: Paduana hispanica; Ricercar brevis; Mein junges Leben
>   hat ein End.

Organ at Millam.

ROLAND. *Early Wallonian Organs.*   ***684**
Monumenta Belgicae Musicae 14.

BABOU: Pièces.
BUSTON: Dialogue et Duo sur les cornets et les tierces.
DUMONT: Suite (Grave, Prélude, Pavane, Courante, Allemande).
HOYOUL: Dominus regit me.
LOHET: Canzone; Media vita; Psalms 9, 51, 125.

Organ in Silly, Hennegau.

SCHOONBROODT. *Orgelmusik des Barock aus den belgischen*   **685**
Niederlanden.
Schwann Musica Sacra AMS 93 [1968].

BABOU: Fantaisie du cornet; Fantaisie pour trompette No. 1; Fantaisie pour trompette basse et haute, No. 8; Pièce No. 1; Sujet varié; Tantum ergo.
HELMONT: Fugas I, II, III, V.
KERCKHOVEN: 8 Versetten im VIII. Kirchenton; Fantasia (C); Fuga (G).

Pfarrkirche, Blankenheim/Eifel.

SLUYS. *Alte Orgeln in Flandern: Haringe.*   ***686**
Monumenta Belgicae Musicae 6.

KERCKHOVEN: Fantasia (C); Fugue (a); Praeludium & Fuga (d); Versetten 1-5.
ROBSON: Präludien und Versetten, Tones I-VIII.

Pieter and Lambert van Peteghem organ (1778), Haringe (West Flanders).

SLUYS. *Organa belgica,* vol. 3.   ***687**
Zephyr Z 06 (Production of Schott Frères, Brussels).

BABOU: Fantaisie des trompettes basses et hautes; Pièce de cornet; Salve Regina.
CHAUMONT: Suite du 2e ton.
DUMONT: Suite (d).
SCRONX: Echo Fantasies (C, F).

Picard (?) organ (1711-?), St. Martin's Church, Gronsveld, Netherlands.

TALSMA. *Die niederländische Orgelschule.* See **87**.   **688**

VERSCHRAEGEN. *Early Organs in Flanders.*   ***689**
Monumenta Belgicae Musicae 29.

    ANONYMOUS: Gavotte.
    CORNET: Fantasia, Tone VIII; Courante.
    FIOCCO: Suites I and II.
    GHEYN: Prelude and Fugue (g).
    ISAAC: Zwischen Berg und tiefem Tal.
    KERCKHOVEN: Versetten I-IV.
    LOEILLET: Gigue.
    OBRECHT: Hélas mon bien.
    RAICK: Gavotte.
    SCRONX: Echo.

St. Bavo, Gent; Machelen bei Deinze; Haringe (West Flanders).

VERSCHRAEGEN. *Early Organs in Flanders.*   ***690**
Monumenta Belgicae Musicae 30.

    CALDARA: Bicinium.
    CHAUMONT: Suite III.
    FIOCCO: Suite II.
    GHEYN: Fugue (f); Sicilienne.
    HELMONT: Fugues (e, G).
    KERCKHOVEN: Versetten I-V.
    SCRONX: Echo.

Pieter and Lambert van Peteghem organ (1778), Haringe (West Flanders).

VERSCHRAEGEN. *L'Encyclopédie de l'orgue,* vol. 15: *L'Orgue*   **691**
des Flandres.
Erato EDO 215.

    BRUMEL: Bicinium.
    CHAUMONT: Prélude (Suite III).
    FIOCCO: Gavotte.
    GHEYN: Sicilienne; Fugue (f).
    HELMONT: Fugues (G, b).
    KERCKHOVEN: Salve Regina.
    SCRONX: Echo.

For organ, see **690**.

Individual Composers

Chaumont, Lambert

SCHOONBROODT. *Livre d'orgue.*   ***692**
Musical Heritage Society 1265/6/7. 3 LPs. (Duplicates Schwann
[Musica Sacra] 102/104.)

Isnard organ, St-Maximin, Provence.

Cornet, Pieter
Complete Works

FERRAND. *L'Encyclopédie de l'orgue,* vols. 33-34: *Pieter*   **693**
Cornet, Intégrale de l'oeuvre.
Erata EDO 233/4. 2 LPs.

Organ of the Bonifaciuskerk in Medemblik (Borstwerk, 16th c.; Hoofdwerk,
17th c.; Rugwerk, 18th c.).

Review:
> *Organ Yearbook* 6 (1975): 171-72.

SLUYS.   ***694**
Monumenta Belgicae Musicae 18/19. 2 LPs.

Goynaut/Peteghem/Anneessens organ, St. Mary's, Lombeek.

Kerckhoven, Abraham van den

SLUYS. *Orgelmusik aus den alten Niederlanden.*   ***695**
Disco Center (Kassel) Dic 3.

> Fantasies (c, e, F, G); Fugues (a, C); Prelude and Fugue (G); Verset-
> ten V, VII.

SLUYS. *Organa belgica,* vol. 1: *Abraham van den Kerckhoven.*   ***696**
Zephyr Z 03. (Production of Schott Frères, Brussels.)

Fantasias (c, d, e, F, G); Fugues (C, a); Prelude and Fugue (G); Verses, Tones V, VII.

18th-century organ, attributed to Dominique Berger, Zuienkerke.

Review:
Diapason 69/11 (November 1978): 7.

Sweelinck, Jan Pieterszoon
Complete Works

KOOPMAN.   ***697**
Telefunken 6.35 374. 5 LPs.

Compenius organ (1612-16), Frederiksborg Castle; Huess (1669-73)/Schnitger organ, St. Cosmae, Stade.

Sweelinck, Jan Pieterszoon
Selected Works

BIGGS. *Variations on Popular Songs.*   **698**
Columbia CSP AMS-6337. (formerly ML 5737 [1962].)

> Balletto del Granduca; Est-ce Mars; Mein junges Leben hat ein End; More Palatino; Unter den Linden grün; Von der Fortuna.

Flentrop organ, Busch-Reisinger Museum, Harvard University.

CHAPELET. *Orgues historiques,* vol. 16: *Frederiksborg.*   **699**
Musique de Tous les Temps OH 16 [1967]. A 45-rpm recording accompanied by a multi-page booklet (in French) on the organ.

> Carmen magistra Pauli; Prooemium (d); Von der Fortuna. (The remainder of the disc contains improvisations by Chapelet.)

Compenius organ (1612-16).

DARASSE. *L'Encyclopédie de l'orgue,* vol. 55.   **700**
Erato EDO 255.

Allein Gott in der Höh sei Ehr; Echo Fantasy; Een Kindekeyn is ons geboren; Fantasia cromatica; More Palatino; Onder een Linde groen; Ricercar (a); Toccata (a).

LEONHARDT. *Fantasien, Toccaten und Variationen für Orgel.*   ***701**
EMI 1C 065 99 608.

Da pacem; Echo Fantasy 12 (d); Fantasia 4 (d); Hexachord Fantasy 5; Puer nobis nascitur; Toccata 17 (a).

Metzler organ (1971), Jacobskerk, The Hague.

LEONHARDT.   ***702**
Cambridge CR 3508 [1962].

Echo Fantasy; Est-ce Mars; Fantasia; Ich ruf zu dir; More Palatino; Paduana lachrimae; Toccatas 20 and 23; Von der Fortuna.

F. C. Schnitger organ, Laurenskerk, Alkmaar; early 18th-century French harpsichord.

THIRY. *Amsterdam du XVIIᵉ siècle: Apogée de l'orgue.*   **703**
Arion 37.178. (Reissued as Musical Heritage Society 4069.)

Durch Adams Fall; Echo Fantasies 14, 15; Erbarm dich mein; Fantasies 3, 4, 9; Psalm 116.

Kern organ, Notre-Dame-des-Blancs-Manteaux, Paris.

CHAPTER 16
SPAIN AND PORTUGAL

Anthologies

BEDOIS. *Portuguese Organ Music of the 16th and 17th*   ***704**
Centuries.
Musical Heritage Society 3469 [1976]. (Duplicates Arion 34.284.)

> ANONYMOUS: Obras de primeiro tom sobre "Salve Regina"; Tento
> de 6º tom.
> ARAUXO: Versos de primeiro tom; Tento de 2º tom; Batalla de 6º
> tom.
> CARREIRA: Fantasia de 8º tom; Tento de 2º tom.
> CONCEIÇÃO: Meio registro de 2º tom.
> DOS REIS: Primeiro concertado sobre o canto chão às avessas;
> Terceiro concertado sobre o canto chão às avessas; Tenção; Pues
> mis sol se aussenta morire de Pena; 2 Tenções; Concerto à 3 com
> dous las (meio registro); Tenção; Tenção sobre o quinto Kyrio de
> missa Santa Maria.

F.-H. Clicquot (1717)/Cavaillé-Coll (1861)/Schwenkedel (1971) organ, St-
Thomas d'Aquin, Paris.

BERNARD. *Historic Organs of Europe,* vol. 1: *Sounds of*   **705**
XVIth-Century Spain. See **95**.

BERNARD. *Old Spanish Organ Music.*   ***706**
Musical Heritage Society 3751. 2 LPs. (Duplicates Deutsche Austro-
phon 85 002.)

ANONYMOUS: Canto suelto; Ite missa est.
BRUNA: Tiento; Versets.
CABANILLES: Toccata II.
CASANOVAS: Prelude; Tiento.
DIEGO: Echo; Entrada grande; Entrada real; Paso suelto; Salida de Navidad; Tiento.
ELIAS: Dialogo.
LLUSA: Versets I-III.
SANTA MARIA: Paso suelto.
SOTO: Tiento.
VIOLA: Sonatas.

Santa María, Daroca: organ partially from the 15th century, with 17th- and 18th-century additions. Cathedral of Malaga: organ by Julián de la Orden (1780-83).

BIGGS. *Historic Organs of Spain.* See **745.** 707

BIGGS. *Organ Music of Spain and Portugal.* See **97.** 708

CHAPELET. *Orgues des Baléares,* vol. 1. See **101.** 709

CHAPELET. *Orgues d'Espagne. See* **103.** 710

CHAPELET. *Orgues espagnoles: Covarrubias.* See **104.** 711

CHAPELET. *Orgues espagnoles: Salamanca.* See **106.** 712

CHAPELET. *Orgues historiques,* vol. 7: *Covarrubias.* See **108.** 713

CHAPELET. *Orgues historiques. Le Monde de l'orgue No. 10:* *714
Orgues de Castille, part 1.
Harmonia Mundi HM 1.208.

ANONYMOUS (18th c.): 5 Canciones para clarines y trompetas.
ARAUXO: Lauda Sion; Tiento de medio registro de baxón de Xº tono.
CABEZON: Tiento "Dic nobis Maria"; Tientos, tones I, IV.
CASANOVAS: Pasa numero siete.
LOPEZ: 3 Versos de medio registro.
MESTRES: 4 Piezas para organo; Tocata, Cantabile amoroso, Marcha por clarines, Tocata pastoril.
ROBERDAY: Fugue et caprice sur le même sujet.

Organs at Villasandino and Melgar de Fernamental.

CHAPELET. *Orgues portugaises: São Vicente de Fora, Lisbon.*   **715**
Harmonia Mundi HMU 704 and HMS 30 704.

ANONYMOUS: 7 Versos varios; Obra e tiento de primer tom.
ARAUXO: Batalla de 6º tom; Obra de primer tom; Tiento de meio registro de baxón de 9º tono; Tiento de 4º tono.
CABANILLES: Tiento No. 23 por Alamire; Toccata II de mano izquierda; Pasacalle II.
CONCEIÇÃO: Meio registro de 2º tom accidental.
DOS REIS: Concerto sobre o 6º tom.

Organ from ca. 1780 by an unknown builder.

COCHEREAU and JONES. *Portugal's Golden Age,* vols. 4/5.   **716**
Philips 6730.011. 2 LPs.

CARREIRA: Fantaisie.
CARVALHO: Allegro (D).
COELHO: 5 Versos sobre "Ave maris stella."
DOS REIS: Concertos 22, 24, 30, and 31; Variations on "Ave maris stella."
SEIXAS: Fugue (a); Fugue No. 76 (a); Sonata (A); Sonatas 48 (G), 15 (c), 29 (d), 74 (a), 75 (a); Toccatas 6 (C), 31 (d), 37 (e), 77 (Bb).

São Vicente de Fora, Lisbon, organ from ca. 1780 by an unknown builder.

LITAIZE. *Les Sommets de l'orgue: Anciens Maîtres d'Espagne*   **717**
et d'Italie. See **823**

LLOVERA. *Hispaniae Musica,* vol. 5: *Orgelmeister des 17.*   **718**
Jahrhunderts.
Deutsche Grammophon (Archive) 198 456 [1969].

> BERNABE: Tiento de falsas de septimo tono.
> BRUNA: Tiento de tiple de primer tono; Medio registro bajo.
> BROCARTE: Tiento de primer tono.
> CABANILLES: Toccata IV de quinto tono.
> DURON: Tiento de primer tono.
> HEREDIA: Tiento de falsas de 6º tono; Pange lingua; Salve lleno.
> PERANDREU: Pange lingua a 4 sobre bajo.
> SOLA: Tiento de primer tono.
> XARABA: Obra accidental No. 1.
> XIMENEZ: Batalla de 6º tono; Pange lingua a 3 sobre tiple.

Three organs: La Seo, Zaragoza (15th-century Gothic case and 18th-century pipework); "Emperor's organ," Cathedral of Toledo (casework from 1543-49, but most of the pipework from the 17th century); Bosch organ (1778), Royal Chapel of the Palace of the Oriente, Madrid.

LLOVERA, organ; ESCOLANIA DE MONTSERRAT, dir.   **719**
SEGARRO. *Hispaniae Musica,* vol. 2: *Meister des Barock.*
Deutsche Grammophon (Archive) 198 453 [1969].

Organ works:
> AGUILERA: Tiento de falsas de 4º tono.
> ALVARADO: Tiento sobre el Pange lingua.
> BRUNA: Tiento de primer tono.
> CABANILLES: Paseos II.
> DEL VADO: Tiento de primer tono.
> ELIAS: Andante-Allegro.
> XARABA: Obra accidental.

Choral works by:
> CERELOS and DURON.

For organs, see **718**.

Review:
> *Music/The AGO and RCCO Magazine* 9/4 (April 1975): 14.

MERSIOVSKY. *Die Orgel in São Vicente de Fora, Lissabon.*   **720**
Harmonia Mundi-BASF 2522042-7 [1974].

ARAUXO: Meio registro.
CARREIRA: Tento a quatro de 2º tom (No. 8); Fantasia a quatro de 4º tom (No. 18).
COELHO: Segundo tento de segundo tom (No. 4); Primeiro Kyrio do primeiro tom por C sol fa ut; Segundo Kyrio do mesmo tom; Terceiro Kyrio do mesmo tom; Quarto Kyrio do mesmo tom; Quinto Kyrio do mesmo tom.
CONCEIÇÃO: Meio registro de dous contra baixos, 1º tom.
DOS REIS: Primeiro concertado sobre o canto chão às avessas; Nono concertado sobre o canto chão às avessas; Primeiro concertado sobre o canto chão de Ave maris stella; Oitavo concertado sobre o canto chão de Ave maris stella.

Organ from ca. 1780 by an unknown builder.

Review:
Musik und Kirche 45/6 (November-December 1975): 309.

RILLING. *Spanish Organ Music.*   *721
Turnabout TV 34 097S.

ARAUXO: Tiento (A); Tres glosas sobre el canto llano de la Immaculada Concepción; Tiento (D).
CABANILLES: Pasacalles (G); Toccata de mano izquierda; Batalla imperial; Pasacalles (D).
CABEZON: Variaciones sobre el canto del caballero; Pavana.

Gedächtniskirche, Stuttgart.

TORRENT. *L'Encyclopédie de l'orgue,* vol. 14: *L'Orgue ibérique.*   722
Erato EDO 214.

ELIAS: Te Deum (Entrada); Salve Regina.
FREIXANET: Sonata (E♭).
SOLER: Sonata No. 67 (F).
VINYALS: Sonata No. 16.

Santa María of Mahon, Minorca.

TORRENT. *Portugaliae musica,* vol. 4: *Orgelwerke des 16.*   723
Jahrhunderts. See **119.**

URIOL. *Antologia de musica antiqua Aragonesa.*   **724**
Discos Movieplay 23.0070/0 F-G.

> BRUNA: Tiento sobre la Letania de la Vergen; Tiento de medio registro
>   de bajo.
> HEREDIA: Ensalada; Pange lingua.
> NASARRE: Toccata de primer tono.
> SOLA: Primer tiento de primer tono.
> XIMENEZ: Otra batalla de 6⁰ tono.

La Seo, Zaragoza: organ with 15th-century Gothic case and 18th-century
pipework.

Individual Composers

Arauxo, Francisco Correa de

MERSIOVSKY. *Francisco Correa de Arauxo: Orgelwerke.*   ***725**
EMI 1C 065-99 679.

> Tientos 10, 15, 16, 28, 34, 37, 47, 52, and 54.

Leonardo F. Davilla organ (1745-55), Cathedral of Granada.

TERNI. *History of Spanish Music,* vol. 9: *Organ Music of*   ***726**
Arauxo.
Musical Heritage Society 3030. (Duplicates Hispavox HHS 14 and Erato STU
70.778.)

> Tientos V de 5⁰ tono, XV de 4⁰ tono, XVI de 4⁰ tono, XXIII de 6⁰
> tono, XXVI de medio registro, XLIII de medio registro; 3 glosadas
> sobre el canto llano de la Immaculada Concepción.

"Gospel" organ by Echevarría (1747), Cathedral of Segovia.

Review:
> *Organ Yearbook* 6 (1975): 172.

Cabanilles, Juan José

MERSIOVSKY.   **727**
Harmonia Mundi-BASF EA 229-041 [1976].

Gallardas I; Tientos III, IV, IX, XII, XV; Toccata II; Pasacalles II.

J. Verdalonga organ (1797), Cathedral of Toledo.

ORTIZ. *History of Spanish Music,* vol. 10: *Juan Cabanilles on*   ***728**
the Organs of Daroca and Toledo.
Musical Heritage Society 3069. (Duplicates Hispavox HHS 9 and Erato STU 70 779.)

> Batalla imperial; Gallardas I de primer tono; Pasacalles I de primer tono, IV de 4º tono; Paseos II; Tientos II de falsas de primer tono, XII de falsas de 4º tono, XVI llano de 5º tono, XVII sobre "Pange lingua," 5º tono; Tiento de battalla de 5º tono; Toccata II de mano izquierda de 5º tono.

Organs: Santa María, Daroca (partially from the 15th century, with 17th- and 18th-century additions); "Emperor's organ," Cathedral of Toledo (casework from 1543-49, but most of the pipework from the 17th century).

Review:
> *Organ Yearbook* 6 (1975): 172.

TORRENT. *Die spanischen Trompeten.*   ***729**
Schwann (Musica Sacra) 2569.

> Tientos III, IV, XXIII; Gallardas V; Pasacalles II, III; Batalla imperial.

Organ at Santa María, Daroca (partially from the 15th century, with 17th- and 18th-century additions).

Reviews:
> *Organ Yearbook* 3 (1972): 117-18; ibid., 8 (1977): 94.

Coelho, Manuel Rodriguez

SIBERTIN-BLANC. *L'Encyclopédie de l'orgue,* vol. 19: *L'Orgue*   **730**
ibérique.
Erato EDO 219.

Excerpts from *Flores de Musica:* Kyrie do 6º tom (No. 51); Kyrie do
3º tom (No. 53); 2º Tento do 2º tom (No. 5); Kyrie do 8º tom (No.
52); Primeiro tento do 2º tom (No. 4); Ave maris stella, 3 versets;
Primeiro tento do 7º tom (No. 19).

Flentrop organ (1964), Cathedral of Lisbon.

MIXED NATIONAL ORIGIN

Anthologies

ALAIN. *Organ Music before Bach.*   **731**
Musical Heritage Society 627.

> ARAUXO: Tiento de 4º tono a modo de canción.
> BLOW: Toccata.
> BRUHNS: Praeludium und Fuge (e).
> CERNOHORSKY: Fugue (a).
> FRESCOBALDI: Toccata; Canzon.
> GRIGNY: Cromorne en taille à 2 parties.
> PACHELBEL: Fantasia (g).
> SWEELINCK: Mein junges Leben.

Joyeuse/Gonzalez organ, Cathedral of Auch.

ALAIN, organ; CAILLAT CHORALE; BRASS ENSEMBLE;   ***732**
PAILLARD CHAMBER ORCHESTRA, dir. CAILLAT. *Sacred Music
in the Cathedral of Chartres.*
Musical Heritage Society CC9L. (Duplicates Erato STU 70 248 [1964].)

Organ works:
> JULLIEN: Suite, Mode VII.

Instrumental and vocal works by:
> BRUMEL, CAURROY, and ROBERT.

ANDERSON. *King of Instruments: A Program of 18th-Century*   **733**
Organ Music.
Aeolian Skinner 329.

C. P. E. BACH: Fantasie und Fuge (c).
J. S. BACH: An Wasserflüssen Babylon, S. 653b; Ricercar a 6 (from *Musical Offering*), S. 1079.
CABANILLES: Batalla imperial.
J.-F. DANDRIEU: Suite (D).
GREENE: Voluntary XIII (G).
SEGER: Fuga (f).
ZIPOLI: 4 Versos; Canzona (g).

Aeolian-Skinner organ (1970), Zumbro Lutheran Church, Rochester, Minnesota.

ANTONINI, CHAPUIS, and SAORGIN. *Orgues de France.*   ***734**
Harmonia Mundi HM 756.

CIMA: Canzone alla francese "La Novella."
CLERAMBAULT: Récit de nazard.
G. CORRETTE: Concert pour les flûtes; Dialogue de voix humaine.
F. COUPERIN: *Messe des Paroisses:* Voix humaine (Gloria); Duo de tierces (Elévation); Dialogue sur les grands jeux; *Messe des Couvents:* Offertoire.
DAQUIN: Noel VI.
DORNEL: Dialogue sur les anches; Récit de cornet.
FRESCOBALDI: Toccata per l'elevazione.
MARCHAND: Pièce en la mineur; Basse de cromorne; Quatuor.
MARTINI: Sonata sui flauti.
ROBERDAY: Fugue II et Caprice sur le même sujet.

Instruments: Jullien organ (1690), Roquemare; Isnard (1772), Saint-Maximin; Royer (1648)/Mentasti (1827), L'Isle-sur-la-Sorgue; Piantanida at Manosque; Piantanida (1820) at Notre-Dame-des-Doms, Avignon.

ARNER. *Den märkliga Orgeln in Tjällmo.*   **735**
Proprius 7728.

CARVALHO: Allegro.
CZERNOHORSKY: Fugue (a).
HAYES: Pastorale.
HINE: Selections from *Harmonia Sacra*.
HOFHAIMER: Ave maris stella.
MARTINI: Sonata sui flauti No. 1.
PASQUINI: Folie d'Espagne.
PODBIELSKY: Praeludium (d).

SCHEIDT: Cantilena anglica fortunae.
STANLEY: Voluntary Op. 5, No. 1.
ZIPOLI: Offertorio.

Early 18th-century Swedish organ, built with 15 notes to the octave to allow mean-tone temperament through most keys. Restored in 1969.

Review:
Organ Yearbook 10 (1979): 182-83.

ARNER. *Orgues historiques,* vol. 17: *Aatvidaberg.*   **736**
Musique de Tous les Temps OH 17 and HM 4512 [1967]. A 45-rpm recording accompanied by a multi-page booklet (in French) on the organ.

    KERCKHOVEN: Fugue (C).
    SCHEIDT: Cantilena anglica fortunae.
    WECKMANN: Canzona (d).

Johan Wistenius organ (1751), Aatvidaberg near Linköping (Oestergotland). Restored by Moberg (1955).

AUBERT. *Orgelmusik in der Dorfkirche Tempelhof.*   **737**
Berliton SP 102 [1975].

    C. P. E. BACH: Sonata (d).
    J. S. BACH: Kommst du nun, Jesu, S. 650.
    BYRD: The Flute and the Droome.
    F. COUPERIN: Tierce en taille.
    MOZART: Leipziger Gigue, K. 574.
    SCHEIDT: Warum betrübst du dich, mein Herz.
    TUNDER: In dich hab' ich gehoffet, Herr.

BÄSSLER and RIETHMÜLLER. *Orgelmusik aus Altenwerder.*   ***738**
Pelca PSR 40622 [1978].

    BACH: Präludium und Fuge (A), S. 536; Fuga sopra il Magnificat, S. 733.
    BRUHNS: Präludien und Fugen (e, g).
    FRESCOBALDI: Canzona prima (1637).
    GALUPPI: Sonata (G).
    HANFF: Auf meinen lieben Gott.
    KREBS: Herzlich lieb hab ich dich; Fuge (Bb) über B-A-C-H.
    PASQUINI: Introduzione e pastorale (G).

Beckerath organ (1969), Altenwerder.

BENESCH. *Sur l'orgue en bois de la Chapelle d'Argent*   **739**
d'Innsbruck.
Philips 835 761 LY.

> BACH: Entrata.
> BANCHIERI: Dialogo per organo.
> FRESCOBALDI: Canzon dopo l'Epistola; Toccata per l'elevazione.
> GIBBONS: Fancy in C fa ut.
> ISAAC: Innsbruck ich muss dich lassen.
> KAUFFMANN: Schmücke dich, o liebe Seele.
> KRIEGER: Ricercar.
> MOZART: Adagio, K. 617a.
> SECHTER: Versetten, Op. 22.
> STANLEY: Voluntary VII.
> STRUNGK: Lass mich dein sein und bleiben.
> ZIPOLI: Pastorale; 3 versets.

16th-century Italian organ, Silver Chapel of the Hofkirche, Innsbruck.

BERG. *Faglarna och Källorna.*   **740**
Proprius 7742.

> BACH: Chorale, S. 656.
> BUXTEHUDE: Prelude and Fugue (f♯).
> LEBEGUE: Noël "Cette journée."
> MESSIAEN: *Messe de la Pentecôte,* No. 4.
> PACHELBEL: Ciacona (f).
> SWEELINCK: Est-ce Mars.
> VIVALDI: Flute Concerto No. 4, 2nd movement.

Marcussen organ, Vånga, Sweden.

Review:

> *Organ Yearbook* 10 (1979): 182-83.

BIBO. *Pape Orgeldokumente,* vol. 12: *Orgel in der Valentinus-*   **741**
Kirche Kiedrich. See **333**.

BIGGS, organ; VAN DER LEK, English horn. *Famous Organs*   ***742**
of Holland and Northern Germany.
Columbia M-31961 [1973].

BACH: Allein Gott in der Höh sei Ehr.
BUXTEHUDE: Lobt Gott ihr Christen allzugleich; Fanfare (Sinfonia)
   from Cantata *Ihr lieben Christen, freut euch nun.*
CORNET: Courante met Varieties.
KOETSIER: Partita for English Horn and Organ.
PAUMANN: Mit ganczem Willen.
SCRONX: 2 Fantasias in Echo Style (G, F).
SWEELINCK: Fantasia (a); 2 Echo Fantasies (d, a).
TELEMANN: Aria (c).

Anonymous choir organ (early 1500s), Laurenskerk, Alkmaar; Flentrop organ (1958), Church of the Holy Sacrament, Breda; Niehoff organ (1551-1553), Johanniskirche, Lüneburg. Schnitger organs in Holland: Dutch Reformed Church, Uithuizen (1700); Grote Kerk, Zwolle (1720); Laurenskerk, Alkmaar (1725). Schnitger organs in Germany: Dedesdorf; Lüdingworth (1598/1682).

BIGGS. *The Four Antiphonal Organs of the Cathedral of*   ***743**
Freiburg.
Columbia M33514 (quadraphonic sound).

BANCHIERI: Dialogo per organo.
BUXTEHUDE: Toccata and Fugue (F).
CAMPRA: Rigaudon (A).
HANDEL: *Aylesford Pieces:* Fugue, Saraband, Impertinence; Awake
   the Trumpet's Lofty Sound (from *Samson*); Pomposo (*Water
   Music*).
KREBS: Fugue on B-A-C-H.
MOZART: Adagio (C), K. 356.
PURCELL: Rondeau and Ayre (G) (from *Abdelazer*); Trumpet Tune
   (from *Bonduca*); Trumpet Tune (from *The Indian Queen*); Volun-
   tary (C), attributed to Purcell.
SOLER: The Emperor's Fanfare.

Four modern instruments: two by Rieger, one by Marcussen, one by Spaeth.

Review:
   Music/The AGO and RCCO Magazine 9/12 (December 1975): 13.

BIGGS. *Historic Organs of Europe: Switzerland.* See **2.**   **744**

                                                                     *745
BIGGS. *Historic Organs of Spain.*
Columbia MS 7109 [1968].

ANGLES: Aria (d).
ANONYMOUS (16th c.): 7 Fabordones.
CABANILLES: Batalla imperial.
J.-F. DANDRIEU: Duo, En cors de chasse sur la trompette.
MILAN: Pavanna.
B. PASQUINI: Partite sopra la Aria della Folia de Espagna.
SEIXAS: Sonata (g); Toccata (d).
SOLER: Emperor's Fanfare; Sonata for the Clarines (A).
VALENTE: La Romanesca; Lo Ballo dell'Intorcia.

"Gospel" organ by Echevarría (1747), Cathedral of Segovia; "Gospel" organ by Echevarría (1744), new Cathedral at Salamanca; Bosch organ (1778), Royal Palace, Madrid; "Emperor's organ," Cathedral of Toledo (with casework from the 16th century, most pipework from the 17th century).

BIGGS, organ; COLUMBIA SYMPHONY ORCHESTRA, dir.   ***746**
ROZSNYAI. *24 Historic Organs.*
Columbia MG 31207 [1972]. 2 LPs. (A composite of excerpts from earlier releases.)

ANONYMOUS: Packington's Pound; Fabordon.
BACH: Lobt Gott, ihr Christen, allzugleich; Vom Himmel hoch; Toccata (d); Toccata (Dorian); Fugue (C).
BUXTEHUDE: Prelude and Fugue (g).
CABANILLES: Batalla imperial.
CLERAMBAULT: Trompette en dialogue.
F. COUPERIN: Offertoire sur les grands jeux.
L. COUPERIN: Fanfare; Rondeau.
DUNSTABLE (attributed): Agincourt Hymn.
FRESCOBALDI: Two Galliards.
HANDEL: Sonata from *The Triumph of Time and Truth.*
HAYDN: Concerto No. 2 (C), movement 1.
LEBEGUE: Basse de trompette.
LEONINUS: Haec dies.
MOZART: Fantasia (f), K. 608; Church Sonata No. 14 (C).
PASQUINI: Variazioni sopra la follia.
PEPPING: Sonne der Gerechtigkeit; Freuet euch, ihr Christen alle.
PURCELL: A Ground in Gamut.
RAISON: Passacaglia (g).
ROBERTSBRIDGE CODEX: Estampie.
SCHEIN: Selection from *Venuskränzlein.*
SOLER: The Emperor's Fanfare.
STANLEY: Allegro.
VALENTE: Lo ballo dell'Intorcia.

WALTHER: Meinen Jesum lass ich nicht.
ZIPOLI: Offertorio.

Organs at: Lüneburg, Stade, Lüdingworth, Norden, Cappel, Sion, Arlesheim, Great Packington, Macclesfield (Cheshire), Staunton Harold (Leicestershire), Haarlem, Zwolle, Uithuizen, Alkmaar, Toledo, Segovia, Salamanca, Madrid, Bologna, Brescia, and Eisenstadt.

BILGRAM, organ; ANDRE, trumpet. *Music for Trumpet and*   ***747**
Organ.
Musical Heritage Society 1064. (Duplicates Erato STU 70.488 and
EMI 1C 065-28272.)

> KREBS: Gott der Vater wohn uns bei; Herzlich lieb hab' ich dich, o
>   Herr; Wachet auf, ruft uns die Stimme; Es ist gewisslich an der
>   Zeit; Liebster Jesu, wir sind hier; Was mein Gott will, das gescheh'
>   allezeit.
> LOEILLET: Sonata for Trumpet and Organ (C).
> TELEMANN: Sonata for Trumpet and Organ (g).
> VIVALDI: Concerto for 2 Trumpets and Organ (C).

Kleuker organ, Eglise Allemande, Paris.

BILGRAM, organ; ANDRE, trumpet. *Music for Trumpet and*   ***748**
Organ.
Musical Heritage Society 3410.

> C. P. E. BACH: Sonata (g).
> BÖHM: Suite (D).
> LOEILLET: Sonata (g).
> PURCELL: Suite (D); Trumpet Overture.

Silbermann/Mühleisen-Kern organ, St. Pierre le Jeune, Strasbourg.

BILLETER. *Konzert auf der Bossard-Orgel in Zursach.*   **749**
Pelca PSR 40 557.

> CLERAMBAULT: Suite, Tone II.
> MENDELSSOHN: Sonata IV.
> MOZART: Fantasie (f), K. 594.
> GEORG MUFFAT: Fugues I-VI; Toccata I.

SEGER: Toccata & Fugue VII.
ZIPOLI: All'elevazione.

F. J. R. Bossard organ (1819), restored by Mathis.

Review:

Organ Yearbook 5 (1974): 143.

BOEKEL, DE KLERK, and LEONHARDT. *Die Orgel: Holland.*   ***750**
Telefunken 6.35 058 DX (also TK 11545/1-2). 2 LPs.

C. P. E. BACH: Sonata No. 4.
J. S. BACH: Chorales, S. 639, 640, 649, 748; Eight Little Preludes and
Fugues, S. 553-560.
F. COUPERIN: Offertoire (*Messe des Paroisses*).
GRIGNY: Cromorne en taille.
REINKEN: An Wasserflüssen Babylon.
SCHEIDEMANN: Praeambulum (d); Resonet in laudibus.

Schnitger organs: Michaelis-Kerk, Zwolle, and the Hervormde-Kerk, Nord-
broek (Groningen). Christian Müller organ, Waalse-Kerk, Amsterdam.

Review:

Organ Yearbook 6 (1975): 168-69.

NOTE: The two discs of this set were previously available separately as follows:
BOEKEL and DE KLERK, *Die alte Orgel: Schnitger-Orgel in der St. Michaelis-Kerk
zu Zwolle,* Telefunken SAWT 9444-B (works of J. S. BACH); LEONHARDT, *Die alte
Orgel: Christian Müller-Orgel der Waalse Kerk in Amsterdam und A. Schnitger-Orgel
der Hervormde Kerk in Noordbroek,* Telefunken SAWT 9521-B (works by ANON-
YMOUS, C. P. E. BACH, COUPERIN, GRIGNY, SCHEIDEMANN, and REINKEN).

BOYER. *L'Orgue historique de Gimont.*   ***751**
Stil Discothèque 2.103S 71.

ARAUXO: Canto llano de la Immaculada Concepción.
BRUNA: Tiento de dos tiples.
GUILAIN: Suite du 3e ton; Cromorne en taille.
RACQUET: Fantaisie.
SCRONX: Echo.
SWEELINCK: Balletto del granduca; Von der Fortuna.
VALENTE: Lo ballo dell'Intorcia.

CHAPELET. *Orgue historique de Frederiksborg.* See **129.**   **752**

CHAPELET. *L'Orgue historique Jullien (1690) de Roquemare.*   ***753**
Harmonia Mundi 932.

> BUXTEHUDE: Jesus Christus, unser Heiland; Wie schön leuchtet der
> Morgenstern; Fugue (C).
> L. COUPERIN: Branle de Basque; Chaconnes (c, F), Duo.
> LANES: Plein jeu; Basses de trompette I and II; Récits de nazard et
> de tierce; Grand jeu; La Piémontaise.
> SCHEIDT: Magnificat, Tone II.
> SWEELINCK: Unter der Linden grüne.

CHAPELET. *Orgues historiques. Le Monde de l'orgue No. 9:*   ***754**
Saint-Siffrein de Carpentras.
Harmonia Mundi HM 1.207.

> ANONYMOUS: Tiento lleno; Ligaduras.
> BACH: Chorales, S. 740, 768.
> BRUNA: Tiento de falsas.
> HEREDIA: Salve 1º tono.
> SCHEIDT: Warum betrübst du dich, mein Herz.

Pascal Quoirin organ (1974).

CHAPELET. *Orgues historiques. Le Monde de l'orgue No. 11:*   ***755**
Orgues de Castille, part 2.
Harmonia Mundi HM 1.209.

> ARAUXO: Canto llano de la Immaculada Concepción, con sus glosas.
> J.-F. DANDRIEU: Magnificat, 6 versets; Plein jeu; Offertoire; Fugues
> I, II; Trio; Cromorne en taille.
> FRESCOBALDI: Toccata avanti il ricercar; Ricercar con l'obligo di can-
> tare la quinta parte.
> LOPEZ: 5 Versos de medio registro.

Santa María and Santa Eulalia organs, Paredes de Nava.

CHAPELET, CHAPUIS, SAORGIN, and WINTER. *Les Orgues*   ***756**
historiques d'Europe, vol. 1.
Harmonia Mundi 580.

ANONYMOUS: 3 Fauxbourdons.
ARAUXO: Canto llano.
COUPERIN: Selections from *Messe des Paroisses*.
DAQUIN: Noël X.
FRESCOBALDI: Ricercare.
MARCHAND: Selections from *Livres d'orgue* I and II.
PACHELBEL: Ricercare (C).
ROBERDAY: Fugue II et Caprice.
SCHEIDT: Warum betrübst du dich, mein Herz.
SWEELINCK: Est-ce Mars; Toccata.
XIMENEZ: Batalla.

Historic organs of Denmark, France, Germany, and Spain: Frederiksborg, Bastia, L'Isle-sur-la-Sorgue, Saint-Maximin, Souvigny, Steinkirchen, Trebel, Covarrubias, and Salamanca.

CHAPUIS. *Michel Chapuis spielt Orgelwerke.*   ***757**
Telefunken-Valois 6.41 872 [1974].

BACH: Praeludium und Fuge (a), S. 543; Toccata (d), S. 565; Trio (d), S. 583; Wachet auf, ruft uns die Stimme, S. 645.
BUXTEHUDE: Fuge (C), BuxWV 174; Jesus Christus, unser Heiland, BuxWV 198; Nun bitten wir, BuxWV 208; Toccata (F), BuxWV 156.
CLERAMBAULT: Basse et dessus de trompette; Récits de cromorne et cornet séparé; Dialogue sur les grands jeux.
DANDRIEU: Allons voir ce divin Gage.
DAQUIN: Noël étranger.

CHAPUIS, organ; SCHOLA MANECANTERIE WALBOURG, dir.   **758**
AUER. *Chant grégorien et orgue: Musique liturgique.*
Productions Kausmaus 0.909.

Organ works:

ATTAINGNANT: Te Deum laudamus.
BÖHM: Chorale variations.
LEBEGUE: Versets à l'orgue.
PACHELBEL: Komm Gott Schöpfer heil'ger Geist.
SCHEIDT: Organ versets.

Vocal works:

Latin hymns and chants from the Ordinary of the Mass, *Cunctipotens Genitor Deus*.

Basilica of Marienthal.

CHAPUIS, DARASSE, HRON, KAUNZINGER, KRAJS,   ***759**
KRUMBACH, NOVAK, PROEGER, ROPEK, SCHOONBROODT,
TORRENT, VACHULKA, and WUNDERLICH. *Orgelmusik aus vier*
Jahrhunderten auf dreizehn historischen Orgeln in Europa.
Schwann (Musica Sacra) AMS 870. 10 LPs.

This box-album is a reissue of 10 records that had previously been issued
individually:

> CHAPUIS: *Alte französische Orgelmeister.*
> DARASSE: *Zwischen Spanien und Frankreich.*
> HRON, KRAJS, NOVAK, ROPEK, and VACHULKA: *Orgeln aus dem*
> *goldenen Prag.*
> SCHOONBROODT: *Tanzstücke aus der Tablatur des Johannes von*
> *Lublin; Orgelmusik des Barock aus den belgischen Niederlanden.*
> TORRENT: *Die spanischen Trompeten.*
> WUNDERLICH: *Norddeutsche Orgelmeister.*

Three records of music beyond the chronological limits of this discography:

> KAUNZINGER: *Schumann auf der Orgel.*
> KRUMBACH: *Beethoven auf der Orgel.*
> PROEGER and BAUER: *Mozart auf der Orgel.*

Of these separate issues the first seven are listed in the present discography
as **214, 218, 163, 92, 685, 729** and **430** respectively. Details of the organs
used and of the compositions performed will be found under these entries.

CHAUVIN, GÖTTSCHE, HASELBÖCK, and VER HASSELT.   ***760**
Historische Orgeln Europas.
Da Camera SM 193 298 [1976].

> ATTAINGNANT: Tablature 2, 5, 7, 15, 21.
> C. P. E. BACH: Pieces for a Musical Clock.
> J. S. BACH: Toccata (E), S. 566.
> BEAUVARLET-CHARPENTIER: Quand Jésus naquit à Noël.
> BEETHOVEN: Präludium II durch alle Tonarten, Op. 39/2.
> J.-F. DANDRIEU: Magnificat versets.
> HANDEL: Clay's Musical Clock — Air, Allegro moderato, Flight of
> the Angel, Gigue, Menuett.
> LEBEGUE: Les Cloches.
> MARTINI: Gavotte.

Organs in Austria, France, and Germany: "Mozart organ," Kajetanerkirche,
Salzburg; "Haydn organ," Cathedral of Eisenstadt; Walcker organ, Seckau
Monastery; F. X. Christoph organ, Basilica of Sonntagsberg; Silbermann
organ, Marmoutier; Clicquot/Gonzalez organ, La Flèche; "Couperin organ,"
St. Gervais, Paris; Gabler organ, Weingarten.

CHORZEMPA, LEHOTKA, LEONHARDT, and PIASETZKI.   *761
Philips 6833 141.

> BACH: Toccata (d), S. 565; Sonata VI.
> MOZART: Fantasia (f), K. 594.
> SWEELINCK: Mein junges Leben hat ein End.

COCHEREAU. *Les Maîtres d'orgue de Chartres.* See **133.**   762

DALTON.   *763
Abbey 602.

> BACH: *Orgelbüchlein* chorales, S. 599-602, 604, 606-09, 611, 613-15.
> BRUHNS: Praeludium (e).
> F. COUPERIN: Récit de tierce en taille (*Messe des Paroisses*).

Frobenius organ, Queen's College, Oxford.

DAMJAKOB. *Orgelkonzert im Dom zu Würzburg.*   *764
Christophorus SCGLX 73 801.

> BACH: Fantasie und Fuge (g), S. 542.
> BÖHM: Praeludium und Fuge (C).
> BUXTEHUDE: Nun lob mein Seel den Herren (3 verses).
> CLERAMBAULT: Suite du deuxième ton.
> DAMJAKOB: Improvisation.

Klais organs, Cathedral of Würzburg.

DE JONG. *Addie de Jong spielt Orgelmusik aus dem 18.*   *765
Jahrhundert.
Canto di Vangelo CV 0 107.

> CASANOVAS: Sonata IV.
> FESCH: Tempo di Gavotte.
> HANDEL: Organ Concerto No. 11: Andante.
> KELLNER: Was Gott tut, das ist wohlgetan.
> KREBS: Toccata and Fugue (E).
> STANLEY: Voluntary I (C).
> WALTHER: Concerto del Sigr. Torelli (a); Herr Jesu Christ, dich zu
> uns wend.

Pels/Leeuwen organ, Goede Herdekerk, Rotterdam/Schiebroek.

DE KLERK. *Die Kleinorgel.* See **134.** **766**

DE KLERK. ***767**
Vista 1 900 (Mixtur V 1 900).

> GIBBONS: Fantasia (C); In nomine.
> D. SCARLATTI: Suite (e).
> SWEELINCK: Balletto del granduca; Fantasia No. 12; O Mensch, be-
> wein dein Sünde gross; Toccata No. 17.
> WALTHER: Concerto del Sigr. Meck (b).

Transept organ, Laurenskerk, Rotterdam.

DIGRIS, LEPNURM, LISSIZINA, and UUSVJALI. *Historische* ***768**
Orgeln in Estland, Lettland, Litauen.
Ariola XC 25 704. (Duplicates Melodia-Aeterna XD 25 704 XDK.) 2 LPs.

> ANONYMOUS: Canzona (*Warsaw Tablature*); Aria da chiesa.
> J. S. BACH: 6 Schübler chorales; Präludium und Fuge (E♭), S. 552.
> W. F. BACH: Orgelkonzert (d).
> BUXTEHUDE: Präludium und Fuge (F).
> F. COUPERIN: Selections from *Messe des Paroisses.*
> PACHELBEL: Toccata (e).
> REGER: Fantasie und Fuge, Op. 135b.
> SWEELINCK: Est-ce Mars.

DISSELHORST and KRAPF. *The Tracker Organ at Iowa.* **769**
University of Iowa Press.

> BACH: Passacaglia; Toccata (d), S. 565.
> CLERAMBAULT: 5 pieces from *Suite du deuxième ton.*
> ERBACH: Canzon in the Phrygian Mode.
> KRAPF: Fantasia on a Theme by Frescobaldi.
> PACHELBEL: Vom Himmel hoch.
> REGER: Dankpsalm, Op. 145, No. 2.

Casavant organ, University of Iowa.

DOERR. *Historische Orgeln Oberrhein.* ***770**
Christophorus SCGLX 73835.

BRUHNS: Prelude and Fugue (G).
GUILAIN: Suite du premier ton.
KELLNER: Was Gott tut, das ist wohlgetan.
MOZART: Andante für eine Walze, K. 616.
WALTHER: Jesu, meine Freude.

Schaxel organ (1804), Evangelische Kirche, Allmannsweier; Silbermann organ, Evangelische Pfarrkirche, Meisenheim; Silbermann organ, Klosterkirche, Offenburg; Silbermann organ (restored by Mühleisen), Katholische Pfarr- und Wallfahrtskirche St. Landolin, Ettenheimmünster.

Review:
Organ Yearbook 8 (1977): 98-99.

DUFOUR. *The Great Organ of St. Laurent, Lausanne.*   *771
VDE-Gallo 30 181.

BOYVIN: Duo, 2e ton.
BUXTEHUDE: Erhalt uns, Herr, bei deinem Wort; In dulci jubilo; Magnificat, Tone I; Prelude, Fugue and Chaconne (C); Fugue (C).
CLERAMBAULT: Basse et dessus de trompette.
G. CORRETTE: Mass, 8e ton: Gloria.
F. COUPERIN: Offertoire (*Messe des paroisses*).
GRIGNY: Dialogue sur les grands jeux.
GUILAIN: Récit de tierce en taille (Suite, 1er ton).
MARCHAND: Suite (d) from *Livre d'orgue* I.

EETVELDE. *Alte Orgeln in Flandern: Watervliet.*   *772
Alpha DB 181.

BACH: Fugue, S. 577.
CABANILLES: Interludes (*Messa degli Angeli*).
CORNET: Toccata, Tone III.
HELMONT: Fugue (e).
KERCKHOVEN: Fugue (a).
LOEILLET: Gavotte.
MARCHAND: *Livre d'orgue* I: No. 12.
RAICK: Andante and Gigue.
STANLEY: Voluntary, Op. 7, No. 8.
SWEELINCK: Toccata No. 17.
ZIPOLI: Partita (C).

EXTERMANN. *Swiss Historic Organs.* See **135.**   *773

FETZ. *Von Purcell bis Bach: Europäische Orgelmusik des Spät-* ***774**
barock.
Calig 30803 [1976].

    BACH: Toccata (d), S. 565.
    DANDRIEU: Magnificat.
    GREENE: Voluntary (c).
    MARTINI: Sonata VI.
    PURCELL: Trumpet Tune and Air.

Rieger organ, Stiftskirche Mehrerau.

FISCHER. *Der Organistenmacher Sweelinck und seine Schüler.* **774.1**
Pelca PSRS 40 564.

    NOORDT: Psalm 24.
    SCHEIDT: Passamezzo-Variationen; Weh, Windchen, weh; Herr
       Christ, der einig Gottes Sohn.
    SWEELINCK: Unter der Linden grüne.

Schuke organ, Pauluskirche, Darmstadt.

GIROD. **775**
Vogue CLVLX 535. 2 LPs.

    ARAUXO: Tiento a modo de canción.
    BACH: Transcription from Cantata No. 147; Toccata (Dorian), S. 538;
       Toccata (d), S. 565.
    CABANILLES: Tiento (Bb); Toccata (C).
    CABEZON: Tiento de 2º tono.
    DANDRIEU: Offertoire.
    DU MAGE: Duo; Fugue; Plein jeu.
    GIGOUT: Toccata (b).
    MARCHAND: Plein jeu.
    NIVERS: Récit de voix humaine.
    OXINAGAS: Fugue (g).
    RAISON: Offertoire.
    WIDOR: Toccata (F).

GROSS, organ; KANTOREI ST. KATHARINEN. *Geistliche Musik* **776**
in der St. Katharinen-Kirche zu Braunschweig. See **352.**

GWINNER, OEHMS, PIPER, and ROVATKAY. *Historische*   ***777**
Orgeln Niedersachsen.
Christophorus SCGLX 75956.

> BACH: Kyrie, Gott Vater in Ewigkeit, S. 672; Christe, aller Welt Trost,
>   S. 673; Kyrie, Gott heiliger Geist, S. 674.
> BÖHM: Wer nur den lieben Gott lässt walten.
> GABRIELI: Cantate Domino.
> GIBBONS: A Ground.
> SWEELINCK and his students: Settings of "Allein Gott in der Höh
>   sei Ehr'."
> WALTHER: Jesu, meine Freude.

Positive from ca. 1590 by an unknown builder, Klaus-Kapelle, Goslar; C.
Treutmann organ (1737), Klosterkirche Grauhof near Goslar; C. Vater organ
(1748), St. Nicolai, Gifhorn; Niehoff/Dropa organ, St. Johannis, Lüneburg.
Works presented on these organs are excerpts from the GDO-Tagung in Han-
nover, 1968.

Review:
> *Organ Yearbook* 3 (1972): 117.

HAMILTON, JOHN. *Organ Music of the Grand Siècle.*   ***778**
Orion ORS 73133.

> ANONYMOUS: Sonata (d).
> BALBASTRE: Noëls 3, 4.
> L. COUPERIN: Chaconnes (F, d).
> SOLER: Sonatas 1, 2.
> SWEELINCK: Chromatic Fantasy; Unter den Linden grünen.
> VIOLA: Toccata for Clarines.

Ahrend organ, University of Oregon.

HARDMEYER and SCHWARB, organ; KIRCHENCHOR MURI,   **779**
dir. SCHWARB. *Musik in der Klosterkirche Muri.*
Pelca PSR 40 518.

Two-manual music played on two organs, either in alternation or in echo:
> KINDERMANN: Magnificat octavi toni.
> PACHELBEL: Werde munter mein Gemüt.
> PURCELL: Echo Voluntary.
> SWEELINCK: Variations on "Soll es sein."
> WALOND: Voluntary (d).

Choral works by:
    MANGON.
V. F. Bossart choir organs (1743-44), Monastery Church, Muri, Switzerland.
Review:
    Organ Yearbook 3 (1972): 118.

HARRASSOWITZ and SCHELLER.   *780
Motette-Ursina M1007.

> BACH: 14 Canons (2 organs).
> BLANCO: Concerto for Two Organs.

Steinmeyer organs, St. Lorenz, Nürnberg.

HARVERSON.   *781
Abbey 664.

> BACH: Prelude and Fugue (c), S. 546.
> G. CORRETTE: Gloria in excelsis Deo.
> DANDRIEU: Offertoire pour le jour de Pâques.
> FRESCOBALDI: Bergamasca; 6 dances.

St. Mary's Priory, London.

HASELBÖCK, F. *Ariadne musica.*   *782
Musical Heritage Society 1634 (duplicates Da Camera SM 93 231).

> J. S. BACH: Petit Labyrinthe harmonique, S. 591.
> BEETHOVEN: Präludium durch alle Tonarten, Op. 39, No. 2.
> CALDARA: Praeambulum.
> FISCHER: Preludes and Fugues from *Ariadne musica.*
> SORGE: Toccata per ogni modi.

F. X. Christoph organ (1775), Basilica of Sonntagsberg.

HASELBÖCK, F. *Barocke Spielereien auf der Orgel.*   *783
Da Camera SM 93 224.

> BACH: In dulci jubilo, S. 751.
> L. COUPERIN: Carillon.

DANDRIEU: Noël "Chantons de voix hautaine."
M. HAYDN: Glockenspiel von Salzburg (3 pieces).
KERLL: Capriccio cucu.
LEBEGUE: Les Cloches.
MARTINI: Pastorale.
GEORG MUFFAT: Aria in C (*Nova cyclopeias harmonica*).
MURSCHHAUSER: Lasst uns das Kindlein wiegen "per imitationem cuculi."
SCHEIDT: Echo ad manuale duplex, forte e line.
SCRONX: Echo.
STORACE: Ballo della battaglia.

Jos. Gabler organ (1737-50), Basilica of Weingarten.

HASELBÖCK, F. *Battle Music for Organ.* ***784**
Musical Heritage Society 1790. (Duplicates Da Camera SM 93 210 [1968].)

BANCHIERI: Battaglia; Canzone italiana dialogo.
BULL: Corante battle.
CABANILLES: Batalla II.
CONCEIÇÃO: Batalha de 5º tom.
FRESCOBALDI: Capriccio sopra la battaglia.
KERLL: Feldschlacht.
KRIEGER: Schlacht.
LÖFFELHOLTZ: Die kleine Schlacht.
XIMENEZ: Batalla de 6º tono.

Hildesheim Cathedral.

HASELBÖCK, F. *Noëls, Pastorellen und andere weihnachtliche* ***785**
Orgelmusik.
Da Camera 193 257 [1976].

J. C. F. BACH: Variations.
BALBASTRE: Quand Jésus naquit.
DANDRIEU: Puer nobis; Joseph est bien marié.
DAQUIN: Noëls VIII and XII.
ESTENDORFFER: Gaillarder natalizantes.
KREBS: Fantasia a gusto italiano.
LEBEGUE: Où s'en vont ces gays bergers?; Or nous dites Marie.
MURSCHHAUSER: Gegrüsst seist du.
RATHGEBER: Pastorellen.

Pfarrkirche Sankt Andrä, Lienz.

HASELBÖCK, F. *Tänze des Barocks.*   ***786**
Berliton 30 006. (Reissued as Musical Heritage Society 4374.)

ANONYMOUS: Ballo; Chorea hungarica; Rund laetum et truncum; Saltus Styriacus; Trompeter Stückl; Ein Andres; Bergamasca; Deutsche Fackell; Sösskentantz; Bassa imperiale; Böhmischer Tanz; Pöllnischer Tanz; Judentanz; Trezza; Türkische Intrada.
L. COUPERIN: Suite.
FRESCOBALDI: Aria detta balletto; Corrente No. 4; Gagliarda No. 3.
KINDERMANN: Suite.
MARTIN Y COLL: Entrada y tres canciones.
B. PASQUINI: Bizzarria.
PURCELL: Suite (*Musick's Hand-Maid*).
SCHEIDEMANN: Ballett; Mascharata.
STEENWICK: Serband.
TRABACI: Galliarda IV.

Biefeld organ (1731-34), St. Willhadi Kirche, Osterholz-Scharmbeck.

HASELBÖCK, H., and M. HASELBÖCK. *Stiftskirche Ossiach:*   **787**
Musik für 2 Orgeln.
Preiser SPR 9809.

BLANCO: Concierto de dos organos.
GUSSAGO: Sonata "La Porcellega"; Sonata "La Leona."
LUCCHINETTI: Concerto a due organi.
PACHELBEL: Two Arias from *Hexachordum Apollinis.*
SCRONX: Echo.
TOMKINS: A Fancy for Two To Play.

Abbey Church of Ossiach: an organ from 1700 by an unknown builder, and a 1969/71 Metzler.

Reviews:
Diapason, March 1977, p. 11; *Music/The AGO and RCCO Magazine* 12/1 (January 1978): 15.

HEINEMANN. *Orgelmusik von Sweelinck, Couperin, Bach.*   ***788**
Motette Ursina 1004.

BACH: Sonata IV; Präludium und Fuge (e), S. 548.
F. COUPERIN: Excerpts from *Messe des paroisses.*
SWEELINCK: Echo Fantasy (d).

Oberlinger organ, St.-Paulus-Kirche, West Berlin.

Review:
Musik und Kirche 47/5 (September-October 1977): 244.

HERBST. *Wolfgang Herbst an der Walcker-Orgel der Sankt-*   **789**
Martini-Kirche Bremen-Lesum.
Musikwissenschaftliche Verlags-Gesellschaft, Ludwigsburg [1976].

   GUILAIN: Suite du premier ton.
   TELEMANN: Trio Sonata (D).

HILDENBRAND. *Die alte Orgel: Orgel der Burgkirche von*   ***790**
Sion; Orgel der Pfarrkirche zu Vouvry.
Telefunken 6.41072 (formerly SAWT 9498-B).

   CLERAMBAULT: Suite du premier ton.
   DAQUIN: Two Noëls.
   MEYER: Kyrie eleison I, II.
   OBRECHT: Fantasy "Salve Regina."
   ZIPOLI: Al post communio; Canzona; Pastorale.

Gothic organ (ca. 1390), rebuilt by Matthias Carlen (1718), restored by Kuhn (1954), at Sion; Jean-Baptiste Carlen organ (1822-31) at Vouvray.

HILDENBRAND. *Die alte Orgel: Wallis/Schweiz.*   ***791**
Telefunken 6.41078 (formerly SAWT 9514-B).

   BUXTEHUDE: Wie schön leuchtet der Morgenstern.
   COUPERIN: Gloria.
   FRESCOBALDI: Toccata per la messa "In Festis B. Mariae Virginis."
   GUILAIN: Grand jeu.
   LEBEGUE: Puer nobis nascitur.
   MARCHAND: Grand jeu.
   PACHELBEL: Fantasia (G).
   SPETH: Toccatas I, VI.

Mathias Carlen organ (1746), Pfarrkirche Maria Geburt in Reckingen (Wallis); organ by an unknown builder (late 18th c.), St. Antonius-Kapelle in Münster (Wallis); organ by an unknown builder (between 1684 and 1779), Liebfrauenkirche in Münster (Wallis).

HILDENBRAND. *Historische Orgeln aus der Schweiz.*   ***792**
Telefunken 6.35059 (formerly released as SAWT 9925-B and
9926-B). 2 LPs.

   BACH: O Lamm Gottes unschuldig, S. 656; Passacaglia.
   BRUHNS: Präludium und Fuge (e).

FRESCOBALDI: Bergamasca; Toccata avanti la messa della Domenica
(*Fiori musicali*).
FROBERGER: Ricercar (e).
GEORG MUFFAT: Toccata No. 11 (*Apparatus musico-organisticus*).
PACHELBEL: Christus, der ist mein Leben.
SICHER: Christ ist erstanden; In dulci jubilo; Resonet in laudibus;
Uss hertzens grund.

V. F. Bossart organ(s), Cathedral of St. Gall; G. Aichgasser organ (1763),
Klosterkirche, Fischingen.

HILDENBRAND. *Historische Orgeln in St. Gallen.*   ***793**
Telefunken 6.41937.

J. S. BACH: Präludium und Fuge (Eb).
DANDRIEU: Magnificat (D).
KREBS: Largo.
SCHLICK: Maria zart.
SICHER: In dulci jubilo; Resonet in laudibus.
WALTHER: Concerto del Sgr. Meck (b).

V. F. Bossart choir organs, Cathedral of St. Gall.

Review:
Musik und Kirche 46/3 (May-June 1976): 139-40.

HORA, KLINDA, and REINBERGER. *Europäischen Orgelland-*   ***794**
schaften: Historische Orgeln in Böhmen und Mahren, set 1.
Ariola-Eurodisc XD 86 900 I [1974]. 2 LPs. (Duplicates a Supraphon release.)

BACH: Fantasie und Fuge (g), S. 542; Toccata (d), S. 565.
BRIXI: Fugue (g).
BULL: Pavane.
BYRD: Fantasia (a).
FRESCOBALDI: Aria detta balletto (C).
HANFF: Ein' feste Burg.
KERCKHOVEN: Präludium und Fuge (C).
KERLL: Canzona (C).
MURSCHHAUSER: Praeambulum, Fuge und Finale.
PACHELBEL: Allein Gott in der Höh sei Ehr'; Praeludium, Fuge und
Chaconne.
SEGER: Praeludium und Fuge (C).
TUNDER: Praeludium (g).
ZACH: Fuge (a).

H.-H. Naundt organ (1670-73), Týn Church, Prague; T. Schwarz organ (1745-46), Nicolas Church, Prague; N. Christeindl organ (1632), Ceský Krumlov; two organs by A. Gartner (1754 and 1756), Monastery Church at Teplá; organ from ca. 1700 by an anonymous builder, Castle Church at Telč; organ by B. Semrád (1764), Monastery Church at Nová Riše; organ by A. Richter (1732), Minorite Church at Brünn; M. Engler organ (1740-45), St. Moritz Church at Olmütz.

**HORA, POTMESILOVA, REINBERGER, ROPEK, and   795
VODRAZKA,** organ; PRAGUE SYMPHONY ORCHESTRA, dir. VALEK.
Organs of Prague.
Supraphon 1-11-0661/62. 2 LPs.

> ANONYMOUS: 2 Tablatures.
> BACH: Fantasie und Fuge (g), S. 542.
> BRIXI: Fugue (g).
> DUPRE: Prelude et Fugue, Op. 7.
> FRESCOBALDI: Aria di balletto.
> PEETERS: Chorals, Op. 39, Nos. 2 and 4.
> SEGER: Fugue (C).
> VANHAL: Concerto (F).
> VODRAZKA: Improvisations (Chorale prelude; Toccata and Fugue;
>   Final; Prelude and Fugue; Trio Sonata).
> ZACH: Fugue (a).

H.-H. Naundt organ (1670-73), Týn Church; an early 18th-century organ, Sv. Šimona a Judy; an 18th-century organ in Sv. Salvátora; Kloss/Rieger organ in U Martina ve zdi; organs in Sv. Cyrila (1898), Sv. Mikuláš and Sv. Jakuba.

Review:
> *Organ Yearbook* 3 (1972): 113.

HURFORD.   *796
Argo ZRG 783.

> BACH: Concerto VI.
> BUXTEHUDE: Toccata and Fugue (F).
> CABEZON: Diferencias sobre el canto llano la alta.
> CARVALHO: Sonata (D).
> DANDRIEU: Le Roy des cieux vient de naître; Adam fut un pauvre
>   homme; A minuit fut fait un réveil; Chrétien que suivez l'église;
>   Joseph est bien marié.

HERON: Cornet Voluntary.
PESCETTI: Organ Sonata (c).
RITTER: Sonatina (d).
SWEELINCK: More Palatino.

Eton College.

HURFORD. *797
Argo ZRG 806.

BACH: Passacaglia.
BUXTEHUDE: Passacaglia (d); Prelude, Fugue and Ciacona (C).
BYRD: Ut, re.
CABANILLES: Pasacalles de 1º tono.
CHAMBONNIERES: Chaconne (G).
FRESCOBALDI: Cento partite sopra passacagli.
PACHELBEL: Ciacona (f).
RAISON: Trio en passacaille.

Our Lady of Sorrows Church, Toronto.

HURFORD, organ; ROWLETT, soprano. *Chorale Variations.* *798
Argo ZRG 835.

BACH: O Gott, du frommer Gott.
BULL: Revenant.
BUXTEHUDE: Wie schön leuchtet der Morgenstern; Trauermusik.
GRIGNY: Veni Creator.

Our Lady of Sorrows Church, Toronto.

ISOIR, organ; GIBOUREAU, oboe. *Orgue et hautbois.* See **142.** 799

JACOB. *Berühmte Orgeln Europas: Silbermann-Orgeln.* *800
EMI 1C 147-29 110/14. 5 LPs.

ANONYMOUS: Es ist das Heil.
J. S. BACH: Komm, heiliger Geist, Herre Gott, S. 651a; Wo soll ich
fliehen hin, S. 646; Fantasie (G), S. 572; Präludium und Fuge (G),

S. 541; Wenn wir in höchsten Nöten sein, S. 668; Präludium und
Fuge (e), S. 548; Toccata (d), S. 565; Sonata VI; Schmücke dich,
o liebe Seele, S. 645; Allabreve; Ich ruf zu dir, S. 639; Präludium
und Fuge (D), S. 532.

BOYVIN: Suite, 4e ton.

G. CORRETTE: Messe, 8e ton.

L. COUPERIN: La Pastourelle; Fantaisie.

DANDRIEU: Magnificat (e).

DAQUIN: Noël étranger.

DU MAGE: Plein jeu; Tierce en taille; Grand jeu.

ERBACH: Canzon, Tone IX.

FISCHER: Präludium primum.

FROBERGER: Fantasia (G); Ricercar (e).

KERLL: Canzona (C).

KINDERMANN: Magnificat Tone VIII.

MARCHAND: Dialogue (*Premier Livre*).

GEORG MUFFAT: Toccata No. 11.

MURSCHHAUSER: Aria pastoralis variata.

NIVERS: Ad coenam; Christe Redemptor; Jesu nostra Redemptio; O
lux beata Trinitas; Veni Creator Spiritus.

J. PACHELBEL: Ricercar (c); Toccata (C); Wie schön leuchtet der
Morgenstern; Werde munter.

W. PACHELBEL: Toccata (G).

SCHERER: Intonatio I.

TITELOUZE: Ave maris stella; Veni Creator Spiritus.

WALTHER: Concerto del Sigr. Albinoni (F).

Five Silbermann organs in the Strasbourg area, plus two instruments — one
by Blasius Schaxel, the other by the Stieffel brothers — that represent a continuation of the Silbermann tradition.

Review:

Music/The AGO and RCCO Magazine 11/12 (December 1977): 9.

JACOB. *Historische Orgeln am Oberrhein.*   **801**
Ariola-Eurodisc 86 777 XDK. 2 LPs.

BACH: In dulci jubilo, S. 751.

F. COUPERIN: Gloria versets.

L. COUPERIN: Passacaglia (g).

DAQUIN: Noël suisse.

DU MAGE: Récit et basse de trompette.

ERBACH: Canzona (g).

FISCHER: Fugues I-VI and Finale.

KERLL: Magnificat secundi toni.

KINDERMANN: Magnificat de quarto tono.
KRIEGER: Präludium und Ricercare (g).
GOTTLIEB MUFFAT: Fuga pastorella.
NIVERS: L'Hymne de la très saincte Trinité.
PACHELBEL: Toccata (F); Fantasie (Eb); Präludium, Fuga und Ciacona (d); Aria Sebaldina; An Wasserflüssen Babylon.
RATHGEBER: Pastorella (C); Aria pastorella.
TITELOUZE: Urbs Jerusalem.
ZACHOW: Allein Gott in der Höh sei Ehr'; Vom Himmel hoch; In dulci jubilo; Nun komm der Heiden Heiland.

JACOB. *Weihnachtliche Musik auf historischen Orgeln gespielt.*   ***802**
EMI 1C 061-28 822.

BACH: Chorales, S. 599, 604, 607.
L. COUPERIN: Pastourelle (d); Fantaisie (g).
DAQUIN: Noël No. 8.
HANDEL: Selections from *Clay's Musical Clock.*
HAYDN: *Flötenuhrstücke,* Nos. 2, 3, 11, and 12.
MURSCHHAUSER: Aria pastoralis variata (Variations I-VII); Gegrüsset seist du (Variations I-XIII); Lasst uns das Kindlein wiegen.
NIVERS: Christe Redemptor omnium, part 1.
J. PACHELBEL: Vom Himmel hoch; Wie schön leucht uns der Morgenstern.
W. PACHELBEL: Toccata (G).
TITELOUZE: Ave maris stella.

JACQUENOD. *Romainmotier.*   ***803**
Studios S. M. B-527.

BANCHIERI: Dialogo per organo.
BÖHM: Herr Jesu Christ, dich zu uns wend.
BOYVIN: Récit; Dialogue de voix humaine.
BRUNA: Tiento sobre la letania de la Virgen.
CABANILLES: Tiento de falsas.
CABEZON: Dic nobis María.
FRESCOBALDI: Aria balletto.
GRIGNY: Dialogue.
MARCHAND: Plein jeu; Quatuor; Basse de trompette.
XIMENEZ: Batalla de sexto tono.

KIRN. *Weihnachtliches Konzert im Friesendom auf Pellworm.*   ***804**
Pelca PSR 40 608.

> J. C. F. BACH: Variations.
> J. S. BACH: Chorales, S. 605, 611; Fantasie (G), S. 572.
> BUXTEHUDE: Wie schön leuchtet der Morgenstern.
> DAQUIN: Noëls 8, 12.
> SWEELINCK: Puer nobis nascitur.
> WECKMANN: Magnificat.

Arp Schnitger organ (1711), restored in 1954, Salvatorkirche on the North
Sea Island of Pellworm.

Reviews:
> *Musik und Kirche* 47/6 (November-December 1977): 290; *Ars organi*
> 26/56 (June 1978): 377.

KLEIN. *Orgel-Musik aus der Basilika St. Johann zu Saar-*   ***805**
brücken.
Saraphon-Schallplattenhaus 150-3501 [1978].

> BACH: Toccata (C), S. 564.
> BUXTEHUDE: Te Deum laudamus.
> CLERAMBAULT: Flûtes; Basse de trompette et dessus de cornet.
> COUPERIN: Dialogue sur la voix humaine.
> G. GABRIELI: Ricercare del 10. tono.
> GRIGNY: Récit de tierce en taille; Dialogue sur les grands jeux.
> ROSSI: Toccata settima.

Klais organ, Basilica of St. Johann, Saarbrücken.

KNITL. *Orgelmusik österreichischer und böhmischer Meister.*   **806**
Pelca PSR 40 577.

> ALBRECHTSBERGER: Fuge (G), Op. 16, No. 5; Komm heiliger Geist.
> CZERNOHORSKY: Fuge (a).
> FUX: Sonata VII.
> HAYDN: Fünf Stücke für die Flötenuhr.
> HERZOGENBERG: Aus tiefer Not, Op. 67, No. 3; Meinen Jesum lass
>   ich nicht, Op. 67, No. 6.
> KUCHAR: Fantasie (g).
> GOTTLIEB MUFFAT: Toccata I and 6 Versetten.
> PITSCH: Fantasie und Fuge (d).
> SEGER: Toccata und Fuge (D).
> VANHAL: Fuge (C).

Walcker organ (1959), Basilica of Seckau.

Reviews:
  Ars organi 25/53 (June 1977): 186-87; *Musik und Kirche* 47/1
  (January-February 1977): 33-34; *Organ Yearbook* 8 (1977): 97-98.

KRAPP. *Orgeln im Deutschen Museum: Edgar Krapp spielt auf*   807
den Orgeln der Musikinstrumentensammlung. See **145.**

KRATZENSTEIN, KLAUS. *Orgelkonzert an der Christensen-*   ***808**
Orgel in Wiesbaden.
Motette Ursina 1009 33 [1979].

   BACH: Pastorale.
   HAYDN: Flötenuhrstücken.
   PACHELBEL: Aria Sebaldina; Vom Himmel hoch.
   A. SCARLATTI: Toccata (A).
   SCHILLING: Selected pieces from *Dreissig Interludien.*

Review:
  Ars organi 27/60 (September 1979): 604.

KRAUS. *Orgue baroque.*   ***809**
Sonopresse UM 64 031.

   ANONYMOUS: Pastorella (C).
   BUXTEHUDE: Magnificat.
   DANDRIEU: Noël (D).
   DAQUIN: Noël (G).
   DESPONSATIONE: Pastorella (C).
   GRÜNBERGER: Pastorella (B♭).
   KÖNIGSPERGER: Pastorella (G).
   GOTTLIEB MUFFAT: Pastorella (B♭); Toccata sexta (F).
   RATHGEBER: Pastorella (G).

KRUMBACH. *Das Orgelporträt: Die Riepp-Orgeln in der Bene-*   ***810**
diktiner-Abtei Ottobeuren.
Psallite PET 117/020 971 [1976].

BACH: Aria variata alla maniera italiana.
MARCHAND: *Premier Livre d'orgue.*

Riepp organs (1757-66), Basilica of Ottobeuren.

Review:

Musik und Kirche 47/1 (January-February 1977): 33-34.

KRUMBACH and OPP. *Music for Two Organs.* See **147**.   **811**

LECOT. *Musique européenne des XVIe, XVIIe et XVIIIe siècles.*   ***812**
Studios S. M. 695.

BUXTEHUDE: Nun komm, der Heiden Heiland.
CLERAMBAULT: Plein jeu du 2e ton.
G. CORRETTE: Cromorne en taille du 1er ton.
M. CORRETTE: Grand jeu du 1er ton.
F. COUPERIN: Dialogue sur la voix humaine (*Messe des Couvents*).
FIOCCO: Adagio (G).
HANFF: Ach Gott, vom Himmel sieh darein.
LANES: Basse de trompette du 1er ton.
WALTHER: Partita (C).
XIMENEZ: Batalla.

LEHOTKA. *Gabor Lehotka: Orgel.*   **813**
Qualiton SLPX 11331.

BACH: Präludium und Fuge (e), S. 533; In dulci jubilo, S. 751.
BUXTEHUDE: Praeludium und Fuga (D); Nun komm der Heiden
    Heiland; Puer natus in Bethlehem; Toccata (F).
DAQUIN: 3 Noëls (G, G, d).
PACHELBEL: Aria Sebaldina; Praeludium, Fuga und Ciacona (d).

St. George's Cathedral, Sopron; believed to be the oldest organ in Hungary, with pipework from 1633, the instrument was restored by the State Organ Building Association in 1957.

LEHOTKA. *Orgel der Kirche zu Sarospatak, 18. Jahrhunderts.*   **814**
Hungaroton 11680.

BACH: Präludium und Fuge (C), S. 531; Wenn wir in höchsten Nöten
   sein, S. 641; Vater unser, S. 683; Nun komm der Heiden Heiland,
   S. 549; Fuge (g), S. 131a.
BÖHM: Präludium und Fuge (C).
BUXTEHUDE: Nun komm der Heiden Heiland; Lobt Gott, ihr
   Christen allzugleich; Toccata und Fuga (F).
GREENE: Voluntary (c).
KERLL: Capriccio cucu.
PACHELBEL: Aria quinta aus *Hexachordum Apollinis.*
SCHEIDT: Variations on a Galliard of John Dowland.
SWEELINCK: Fantasia.

LEHRNDORFER and SCHNAUFFER. *Orgelmusik aus Otto-*   ***815**
beuren.
Christophorus SCV 75 133. 17 cm.

   LUCCHINETTI: Sonata a due organi (D).
   PFEYLL: Sonata a due organi (G).
   PIAZZA: Sonata a due organi (F).
   PURCELL: Echo Voluntary for the Double Organ.

Riepp organs (1757-66), Basilica of Ottobeuren.

LEONHARDT. *Alpenländer.* See **149.**   **816**

LEONHARDT. *Die Dreifaltigkeitsorgel von Ottobeuren.*   ***817**
EMI 1C 065- 99 612 (also Harmonia Mundi HMS 30 855 and HM 99
612).

   C. P. E. BACH: Sonata No. 1.
   F. COUPERIN: Excerpts from *Messe des Couvents* and *Messe des*
      Paroisses.
   KERCKHOVEN: Fantasies 352, 354, 355 (c, c, and e).
   GEORG MUFFAT: Toccata I.

K. J. Riepp "Trinity organ" (1757-66), Basilica of Ottobeuren. Restored by
Steinmeyer.

LEONHARDT. *17th-Century Organ Music.*   **818**
Bach Guild BG 529.

ERBACH: Ricercar IX toni sopra "Io son ferito."
FRESCOBALDI: Toccata prima (1637).
FROBERGER: Toccata.
MERULA: Sonata cromatica.
KERLL: Passacaglia; Toccata cromatica con durezze e ligature.
M. PRAETORIUS: A solis ortus cardine; Alves tumescit virginis.
SCHERER: Toccata.

J. G. Freundt organ (1636/42), Klosterneuburg. Restored by Rieger and
Kuhn.

LINSENMEYER. *Das Orgelporträt: Die Dreifaltigkeitsorgel d.*   ***819**
Benediktinerabtei Ottobeuren.
Psallite PET 115/300 871.

BACH: Präludium und Fuge (E♭).
DANDRIEU: Magnificat (e).
J. KRIEGER: Preludio; Ricercar; Fuga; Passacaglia.

K. J. Riepp "Trinity organ" (1757-66), Basilica of Ottobeuren. Restored by
Steinmeyer.

LITAIZE. *Grand orgue de l'église abbatiale Saint-Pierre de*   ***820**
Solesmes: Inauguration du 22 octobre 1967.
International Pelgrims Group 7.508.

BACH: Chorales, S. 646, 668; Toccata (C), S. 564.
BUXTEHUDE: Ach Herr, mich armen Sünder; In dulci jubilo.
CLERAMBAULT: Plein jeu, Basse de cromorne, Récit de nazard, and
    Caprice sur les grands jeux from *Suite du 2e ton.*
SWEELINCK: Mein junges Leben hat ein' End'.

Schwenkedel organ.

LITAIZE. *L'Orgue Müller de la Maison de la Radio: Programme*   ***821**
de la séance inaugurale.
Charlin SLC 20.

BACH: Fantasie (G), S. 572.
BUXTEHUDE: Toccata (d); Wie schön leuchtet der Morgenstern.
CORRETTE; Noël.
GRIGNY: Plein chant en taille; Fugue à 5; Récit de cornet.
MARCHAND: Dialogue; Pièce en ut mineur.

LITAIZE. *Les Sommets de l'orgue,* vol. 1.   ***822**
Charlin SLC 11 (also Schwann "Musica Sacra" AMS 54).

> BACH: Toccata (d), S. 565; Wachet auf, ruft uns die Stimme, S. 645.
> BUXTEHUDE: Prelude, Fugue and Chaconne (C); Ach Herr, mich
> armen Sünder.
> COUPERIN: Offertoire from *Messe des Paroisses.*
> DAQUIN: Noël (G).
> GRIGNY: Récit de tierce en taille; Fugue à 5.

LITAIZE. *Les Sommets de l'orgue: Anciens Maîtres d'Espagne*   ***823**
et d'Italie.
Charlin SLC 13 (also Schwann "Musica Sacra" AMS 76).

> ARAUXO: Tiento de 4º tono.
> CABANILLES: Tiento No. 2; Tiento No. 5; Toccata No. 6.
> CABEZON: Tiento de primer tono; Diferencias sobre el canto del
> cavallero.
> FRESCOBALDI: Toccata avanti la messa, Canzone dopo l'Epistola,
> Toccata avanti il Ricercar, and Toccata per l'elevazione from *Fiori*
> *musicali*; Ricercar.
> A. GABRIELI: Canzon ariosa; Ricercar del VII tono; Ricercar del VIII
> tono.
> ZIPOLI: Canzona.

Héman (ca. 1649)/Clicquot (1781ff.)/Cavaillé-Coll (1855-57) organ at St.
Merry, Paris. Restored by Gonzalez (1943/47 and 1963).

LUKAS. *Historische Orgeln Oberfranken.* See **391.**   **824**

LUTZ. *Orgelwerke des Barock.*   ***825**
Motette 1 002 [1976].

> BACH: Präludium und Fuge (C); Toccata und Fuge (F).
> F. COUPERIN: Kyrie and Agnus Dei from *Messe des Paroisses.*
> GEORG MUFFAT: Toccata XI.
> SWEELINCK: Fantasia (d); Es ist das Heil uns kommen her.

Ebersmünster (Silbermann); Oude Kerk, Amsterdam; Christophoruskirche,
Wiesbaden-Schierstein.

McVEY.   **826**
Orion ORS 77264.

> CLERAMBAULT: Suite du 2ᵉ ton.
> MARCHAND: Grand dialogue (*Deuxième Livre*).
> SCHEIDT: Warum betrübst du dich mein Herz.

Beckerath organ, Pomona College.

Reviews:

> *Diapason,* September 1977, p. 5; *Music/The AGO and RCCO Magazine* 12/1 (January 1978): 17.

MICHEL. *Die historische Orgel der Klosterkirche Oelinghausen.*   **827**
Le Connaisseur Schallplatten 318-7714.

> ANONYMOUS: German and English dances of the 16th/17th c.
> BACH: Concerto (a), S. 593; 9 chorales from the *Orgelbüchlein.*
> BUXTEHUDE: Auf meinen lieben Gott.
> GREENE: Voluntary.
> Additional works by HOFHAIMER and ISAAC.

Review:

> *Ars organi* 27/60 (September 1979): 607.

MUSCH. *Music for Christmas.*   ***828**
Musical Heritage Society 1468. (Duplicates Christophorus SCGLX 75 948.)

> BULL: Christe Redemptor.
> BUXTEHUDE: Gelobet seist du, Jesu Christ.
> CABEZON: Christe Redemptor.
> DAQUIN: Noel X.
> FRESCOBALDI: Capriccio pastorale.
> MURSCHHAUSER: Aria pastoralis variata.
> SWEELINCK: Puer nobis nascitur.
> ZIPOLI: Pastorale.

Klais organ, St. Konrad Kirche, Freiburg.

NEBOIS, positive organ; KANN, clavichord, hammerklavier and   ***829**
piano; LANGFORT, virginal and harpsichord. *The Sound of Keyboard Instruments.*
Musical Heritage Society 862.

Organ works:
   CABEZON: Tiento del quinto tono.
   SWEELINCK: Est-ce Mars.

Works on other keyboard instruments:
   ANONYMOUS, C. P. E. BACH, W. F. BACH, CLEMENTI, FROBERGER,
   and HAYDN.

Hencke positive (1718); hammerklavier from the late 18th century; 17th-century Ruckers virginal; Neupert harpsichord and clavichord.

OEHMS. *Das Orgelporträt: Die Bambus-Orgel von Las Pinas/*   ***830**
Philippinen.
Psallite PET 168/170 275 [1976].

   ARAUXO: Tiento de 7º tono.
   BRAUN: 8 Liedvariationen über "Du mein einzig Licht" (Philippine
      folk melody).
   CABANILLES: Passacaglia de primer tono.
   CABEZON: Tiento de primer tono.
   LOPEZ: Pange lingua.
   STANLEY: Voluntary I (C).
   ZIPOLI: Offertorium; Elevation; Post communio.

Bamboo organ built by Fray Giego Cera in 1816-24 and restored by Klais in 1976 — a one-manual instrument with divided stops in the Spanish tradition.

Review:
   Ars organi 26/56 (June 1978): 377-78.

OEHMS. *Das Orgelporträt: Die Stumm-Orgel in der ehemaligen*   ***831**
Stiftskirche Sankt Kastor zu Karden-Mosel.
Psallite PET 146.210 973 [1974].

   GRIGNY: Verbum supernum.
   LEBEGUE: Suite du 2e ton.
   PACHELBEL: Ciacona (d); Präludium und Fuge (d); Was Gott tut,
      das ist wohlgetan.

Joh. Michael Stumm organ (1728), former Monastery Church of St. Kastor in Karden/Mosel.

Review:
   Musik und Kirche 45/4 (July-August 1975): 202-03.

PIERRONT. 832
Studios S. M. 30-01.

> BACH: Partita, S. 767.
> BOYVIN: Grand dialogue; Voix humaine; Fugue chromatique; Cromorne; Prélude à 2 choeurs; Basse de trompette; Fonds d'orgue; Trio à 2 dessus; Tierce en taille; Grand dialogue.

PRESTON. *833
Argo XK 13.

> BACH: 6 Schübler chorales.
> MOZART: Fantasies, K. 594, 608.

King's College, Cambridge.

REGIER, organ; BATTEL CHAPEL CHOIR, dir. KRIGBAUM. 834
Mark Levinson Acoustic Recordings MAL 1 [1976].

Organ works:

> BACH: 6 Schübler chorales; Prelude (E♭), S. 552.

Choral works by:

> ANONYMOUS, GREENE, MARENZIO, and TALLIS.

Beckerath organ, Dwight Chapel, Yale University.

REINBERGER. *Europäischen Orgellandschaften: Historische* *835
Orgeln in Böhmen und Mahren, set 2.
Ariola-Eurodisc XC 88 00 I. 2 LPs. (Duplicates a Supraphon release.)

> BACH: Präludium und Fuge (D), S. 532; Partita "Ach, was soll ich Sünder machen."
> BÖHM: Christ lag in Todesbanden.
> BRUHNS: Präludium und Fuge (e).
> BUXTEHUDE: Ciacona.
> CORNET: Toccata, Tone III.
> ERBACH: Canzon a 4 del quarto tono.
> FROBERGER: Ricercare I.
> HANFF: Helft mir Gott's Güte preisen.
> LÜBECK: Präludium und Fuge (E).
> GEORG MUFFAT: Toccata XII.
> SCHLICK: Maria zart.
> SWEELINCK: Mein junges Leben hat ein End'.

Several historic Bohemian and Moravian organs, including the Michael Engler
organ (1740-45) at Olmütz.

Review:
  Musik und Kirche 45/6 (November-December 1975): 309.

For set 1, see **794**.

REUTER, organ and harpsichord; LÜTTMAN, oboe; EGGERS,   ***836**
viola; TRIO RAMEAU. *Musik auf historischen Instrumenten,* series 1.
Fono Schallplatten Münster 123 001/002. 2 LPs.

Organ works (FSM 123 002):
>   BACH: Gelobet seist du, Jesu Christ, S. 722; Wenn wir in höchsten
>   Nöten sein, S. 641; Wer nur den lieben Gott lässt walten, S. 691.
>   COUPERIN: Kyrie eleison, Christe eleison, Qui tollis, and Domine
>   Deus rex coelestis (*Messe des Paroisses*).
>   JULLIEN: Prélude, Cromhorne en taille, Basse de trompette, Fantaisie
>   cromatique, and Dialogue (*Suite du premier ton*).
>   PACHELBEL: Toccata and Ricercar (c).
>   WALTHER: Jesu, meine Freude.

Chamber music (FSM 123 001):
>   RAMEAU, BUXTEHUDE, and TELEMANN.

REUTER, organ and harpsichord; SCHÖNE, baritone; JOCHUM,   ***837**
violin; EGGERS, viola da gamba; SONIUS, flute; LÜTTMAN, oboe.
Musik auf historischen Instrumenten, series 2: *Kammermusik aus westfälischen Wasserburgen; Orgelmusik aus westfälischen Kirchen.*
Fono Schallplatten Münster 123 003/004. 2 LPs.

Organ works (FSM 123 004):
>   BACH: Das alte Jahr vergangen ist, S. 614; Aus der Tiefe, S. 745;
>   Toccata (d), S. 565.
>   BÖHM: Ach wie nichtig, ach wie flüchtig.
>   BRUHNS: Präludium und Fuge (e).
>   BUXTEHUDE: Mensch, willst du leben seliglich.
>   F. COUPERIN: Sanctus, Benedictus, and Deo gratias from *Messe des
>   Paroisses.*
>   KAUFFMANN: Ach Gott, vom Himmel sieh' darein (oboe and organ);
>   Gelobet seist du, Jesu Christ (oboe and organ).
>   PACHELBEL: Toccata (e).

Chamber music and songs (FSM 123 003):
>   BACH, LAWES, RAMEAU, MONDONVILLE, DROSTE-HÜLSHOFF,
>   FÜRSTENAU.

REUTER, organ and harpsichord; JOCHUM, violin; EGGERS,   ***838**
viola da gamba; SONIUS, flute. *Musik auf historischen Instrumenten.*
series 3.
Fono Schallplatten Münster 123 005/006. 2 LPs.

Organ works:
    BACH: Chorales, S. 639, 727; Passacaglia.
    BUXTEHUDE: Präludium und Fuge (f#).
    CLERAMBAULT: Suite du 2ᵉ ton.
Harpsichord works by:
    J. S. BACH.
Chamber music by:
    J. C. F. BACH, J. S. BACH, BIBER, and MARAIS.

REUTER, organ; WALCHA, harpsichord. *Musik auf historischen*   ***839**
Instrumenten, series 4.
Fono Schallplatten Münster 123 007/008. 2 LPs.

Organ works:
    BACH: Präludium und Fuge (c), S. 537.
    BUXTEHUDE: Canzone No. 1; Erhalt uns Herr.
    DU MAGE: *Livre d'orgue.*
Harpsichord works by:
    BACH and KUHNAU.

SCHEIDEGGER. *Konzertante Orgelmusik um Bach.*   ***840**
Calig CAL 30 416.

    C. P. E. BACH: Sonata, Wq. 70:6.
    MARCHAND. Plein jeu, Fugue, Duo, Trio, Tierce en taille, Basse de
    trompette, Récit, and Dialogue from *Livre d'orgue* I.

SCHNAUFFER. *Orgelmeister des Barock.*   ***841**
Christophorus SCGLX 73838.

    FRESCOBALDI: Praeludium und Fuge in g [*sic*].
    FROBERGER: Toccata (d).
    INSANGUINE: Sonata (C).
    KINDERMANN: Magnificat octavi toni.
    PACHELBEL: Fantasia (Eb).
    SCHLICK: Maria zart.

BÖHM: Capriccio (D); Preludes and Fugues (a, g, d).
SWEELINCK: Fantasia No. 3; O lux beata Trinitas; Toccata No. 17 (d).

Arp Schnitger organ (1711), St. Salvator-Kirche, Pellworm.

WEISS. *Weihnachtliche Orgelmusik.*   ***854**
Calig 30 508.

BACH: Canonic Variations on "Vom Himmel hoch"; Chorales, S. 659,
701, 733.
DAQUIN: Noël X.
GRIGNY: Gloria.
ZIPOLI: Canzone V; Pastorale.

Marcussen organ, Aabenraa, Denmark.

WINTER. *Orgues historiques,* vol. 19: *Altenbruch.*   **855**
Musique de Tous les Temps OH 19 [1968]. (Also Harmonia Mundi
HM 4515.) A 45-rpm record accompanied by a multi-page booklet (in French)
on the organ.

BACH: Liebster Jesu, wir sind hier.
BANCHIERI: Dialogo.
BRUHNS: Präludium (e).
BUXTEHUDE: Puer natus in Bethlehem.
ZOILO: Bicinium "Melius illi"; Bicinium "Quare fremuerunt."

St Nicolai, Altenbruch: organ originally from the 15th/16th centuries, but
with several additions, notably those by Klapmeyer (1727-30). Restored by
E. Tolle (1954-57) and by Beckerath (1967) .

ZARTNER. *Rudolf Zartner spielt auf historischen Orgelpositivs.*   ***856**
Colosseum StM 1017. 17-cm. LP.

MURSCHHAUSER: Aria pastoralis variata.
PACHELBEL: Fugue (C).
PESCETTI: Sonata (A).

German National Museum, Nürnberg: a positive organ (ca. 1680) from
Georgenried near Gmund am Tegernsee; a positive organ from Heilbronn
(ca. 1750).

ORGAN WORKS OF J. S. BACH

*In the order of the
Schmieder (BWV or S) numbering.*

Free Works 525-598

525-530 *Sonatas*

525. I (E♭)
526. II (c)
527. III (d)

528. IV (e)
529. V (C)
530. VI (G)

531-552 *Preludes (or Fantasies or "Toccatas") and Fugues*

531. Pr & Fg (C)
532. Pr & Fg (D)
533. Pr & Fg (e)
534. Pr & Fg (f)
535. Pr & Fg (g)
536. Pr & Fg (A)
537. Pr (Fn) & Fg (c)
538. Pr (T) & Fg (d)
539. Pr & Fg (d)
540. Pr (T) & Fg (F)
541. Pr & Fg (G)

542. Pr (Fn) & Fg (g)
543. Pr & Fg (a)
544. Pr & Fg (b)
545. Pr & Fg (C)
546. Pr & Fg (c)
547. Pr & Fg (C)
548. Pr & Fg (e)
549. Pr & Fg (c)
550. Pr & Fg (G)
551. Pr & Fg (a)
552. Pr & Fg (E♭)

553-560 *Eight Little Preludes and Fugues*

553. (C)
554. (d)
555. (e)
556. (F)

557. (G)
558. (g)
559. (a)
560. (B♭)

561-563 *Fantasies and Fugues*

    561. (a)   563. (b)
    562. (c) (unfinished)

564-566 *Three Toccatas*

    564. (C)   566. (E)
    565. (d)

567-581 *Preludes; Fantasies; Fugues*

    567. Pr (C)   575. Fg (c)
    568. Pr (G)   576. Fg (G)
    569. Pr (a)   577. Fg (G)
    570. Fn (C)   578. Fg (g)
    571. Fn (G)   579. Fg (b)
    572. Fn (G)   580. Fg (D)
    573. Fn (C)   581. Fg (G)
    574. Fg (c)

582 *Passacaglia* (c)

583-587 *Trios*   *See also* S. 1027a and Anh. 46

    583. (d)   586. (G)
    584. (g)   587. Aria (F)
    585. (c)

588-591 *Miscellaneous*

    588. Canzona (d)   591. Kleines harmonisches
    589. Allabreve (D)   Labyrinth
    590. Pastorale (F)

592-597 *Concertos*

    592. (G)   593. (a)

594. (C)   596. (d)
595. (C)   597. (Eb)

598   *Pedal Exercitium*

Chorale-based Works 599-771

599-644   *Orgelbüchlein*

OB   S
1   599. Nun komm, der Heiden Heiland
2   600. Gott, durch deine Güte (Gottes Sohn ist kommen)
3   601. Herr Christ, der ein'ge Gottes Sohn (Herr Gott, nun sei gepreiset)
4   602. Lob sei dem allmächtigen Gott
5   603. Puer natus in Bethlehem
6   604. Gelobet seist du, Jesu Christ
7   605. Der Tag, der ist so freudenreich
8   606. Vom Himmel hoch da komm ich her
9   607. Vom Himmel kam der Engel Schaar
10   608. In dulci jubilo
11   609. Lobt Gott, ihr Christen, allzugleich
12   610. Jesu, meine Freude
13   611. Christum wir sollen loben schon
14   612. Wir Christenleut
15   613. Helft mir Gottes Güte preisen
16   614. Das alte Jahr vergangen ist
17   615. In dir ist Freude
18   616. Mit Fried und Freud ich fahr dahin
19   617. Herr Gott, nun schleuss den Himmel auf
20   618. O Lamm Gottes, unschuldig
21   619. Christe, du Lamm Gottes
22   620. Christus, der uns selig macht
23   621. Da Jesus an dem Kreuze stund
24   622. O Mensch, bewein dein Sünde gross
25   623. Wir danken dir, Herr Jesu Christ
26   624. Hilf Gott, dass mir's gelinge
27   625. Christ lag in Todesbanden
28   626. Jesus Christus, unser Heiland
29   627. Christ ist erstanden

254

693. Ach Gott und Herr
694. Wo soll ich fliehen hin
695. Christ lag in Todesbanden
695a. Christ lag in Todesbanden
696. Christum wir sollen loben schon
697. Gelobet seist du, Jesu Christ
698. Herr Christ, der ein'ge Gottes Sohn
699. Nun komm, der Heiden Heiland
700. Vom Himmel hoch da komm ich her
701. Vom Himmel hoch da komm ich her
702. Das Jesulein soll doch mein Trost
703. Gottes Sohn ist kommen
704. Lob sei dem allmächtigen Gott
705. Durch Adam's Fall ist ganz verderbt
706. Liebster Jesu, wir sind hier
707. Ich hab mein Sach Gott heimgestellt
708. Ich hab mein Sach Gott heimgestellt
708a. Ich hab mein Sach Gott heimgestellt
709. Herr Jesu Christ, dich zu uns wend
710. Wir Christenleut
711. Allein Gott in der Höh sei Ehr
712. In dich hab ich gehoffet, Herr
713. Fantasia: Jesu, meine Freude
713a. Fantasia sopra Jesu, meine Freude

714-740   *Miscellaneous Chorale Settings*

714. Ach Gott und Herr
715. Allein Gott in der Höh sei Ehr
716. Fuga super Allein Gott in der Höh sei Ehr
717. Allein Gott in der Höh sei Ehr
718. Christ lag in Todesbanden
719. Der Tag, der ist so freudenreich
720. Ein feste Burg ist unser Gott
721. Erbarm dich mein, o Herre Gott
722. Gelobet seist du, Jesu Christ
722a. Gelobet seist du, Jesu Christ
723. Gelobet seist du, Jesu Christ
724. Gottes Sohn ist kommen
725. Herr Gott, dich loben wir
726. Herr Jesu Christ, dich zu uns wend

727. Herzlich tut mich verlangen
728. Jesus, meine Zuversicht
729. In dulci jubilo
730. Liebster Jesu, wir sind hier
731. Liebster Jesu, wir sind hier
732. Lobt Gott, ihr Christen, allzugleich
733. Fuga sopra il Magnificat
734. Nun freut euch, lieben Christen g'mein
735. Fantasia super Valet will ich dir geben
736. Valet will ich dir geben
737. Vater unser im Himmelreich
738. Vom Himmel hoch da komm ich her
739. Wie schön leucht't uns der Morgenstern
740. Wir glauben all' an einen Gott

741-765 *Miscellaneous Chorales: Youthful, Doubtful, Fragmentary*

741. Ach Gott, vom Himmel sieh darein
742. Ach Herr, mich armen Sünder
743. Ach, was ist doch unser Leben
744. Auf meinen lieben Gott
745. Aus der Tiefe rufe ich
746. Christ ist erstanden
747. Christus, der uns selig macht
748. Gott der Vater wohn uns bei
748a. Gott der Vater wohn uns bei
749. Herr Jesu Christ, dich zu uns wend
750. Herr Jesu Christ, mein's Lebens Licht
751. In dulci jubilo
752. Jesu, der du meine Seele
753. Jesu, meine Freude
754. Liebster Jesu, wir sind hier
755. Nun freut euch, lieben Christen g'mein
756. Nun ruhen alle Wälder
757. O Herre Gott, dein göttlich's Wort
758. O Vater, allmächtiger Gott
759. Schmücke dich, o liebe Seele
760. Vater unser im Himmelreich
761. Vater unser im Himmelreich
762. Vater unser im Himmelreich
763. Wie schön leuchtet der Morgenstern

764. Wie schön leucht't uns der Morgenstern
765. Wir glauben all' an einen Gott, Schöpfer

766-771 *Chorale Variations*

766. Partita: Christ, der du bist der helle Tag
767. Partita: O Gott, du frommer Gott
768. Partita: Sei gegrüsset, Jesu gütig
769. Canonic Variations: Vom Himmel hoch da komm ich her
770. Partita: Ach, was soll ich Sünder machen
771. Variations: Allein Gott in der Höh sei Ehr

802-805 *4 Duette (Clavierübung, Part III)*

802. I (e)   804. III (G)
803. II (F)   805. IV (a)

1027a *Trio in G*

1079 *Musical Offering*

1080 *Art of Fugue*

Anhang II: Doubtful Works

Anh. 42-45 *4 Fugues*

Anh. 42 (F)   Anh. 44 (G)
Anh. 43 (b)   Anh. 45 Bb (B-A-C-H)

Anh. 46 *Trio (c)*

Anh. 47-49   *Chorale-based Works*

    Anh. 47. Ach Herr, mich armen Sünder
    Anh. 48. Allein Gott in der Höh sei Ehr
    Anh. 49. Ein feste Burg ist unser Gott
    Anh. 50. Erhalt uns, Herr, bei deinem Wort
    Anh. 51. Erstanden ist der heilige Christ
    Anh. 52. Freu dich sehr, o meine Seele
    Anh. 53. (Freu dich sehr, o meine Seele)
    Anh. 54. Helft mir Gottes Güte preisen
    Anh. 55. Herr Christ, der einig Gottes Sohn
    Anh. 56. Herr Jesu Christ, dich zu uns wend
    Anh. 57. Jesu Leiden, Pein und Tod
    Anh. 58. Jesu, meine Freude
    Anh. 59. Jesu, meine Freude
    Anh. 60. Nun lob mein Seel den Herren
    Anh. 61. O Mensch, bewein dein Sünde gross
   Anh. 62a. Sei Lob und Ehr mit hohem Preis
   Anh. 62b. Sei Lob und Ehr mit hohem Preis
    Anh. 63. Vom Himmel hoch da komm ich her
    Anh. 64. Vom Himmel hoch da komm ich her
    Anh. 65. Vom Himmel hoch da komm ich her
    Anh. 66. Wachet auf, ruft uns die Stimme
    Anh. 67. Was Gott tut, das ist wohlgetan
    Anh. 68. Wer nur den lieben Gott lässt walten
    Anh. 69. Wir glauben all' an einen Gott
    Anh. 70. Wir glauben all' an einen Gott
    Anh. 71. Fantasia: Wo Gott der Herr nicht bei uns halt
    Anh. 72. *Title lacking.* Moderato. Canon
    Anh. 73. Ich ruf zu dir, Herr Jesu Christ
    Anh. 74. Schmücke dich, o liebe Seele
    Anh. 75. Figured bass: Herr Christ, der einig Gottes Sohn
    Anh. 76. Figured bass: Jesu, meine Freude
    Anh. 77. Variations: Herr Christ, der einig Gottes Sohn
    Anh. 78. Chorale and 6 variations: Wenn wir in höchsten
           Nöten sein

Anh. 88-106   *19 Fugues*

    Anh. 88 (C)   Anh. 91 (D)
    Anh. 89 (C)   Anh. 92 (G)
    Anh. 90 (C)   Anh. 93 (e)

Anh. 94 (e)
Anh. 95 (e)
Anh. 96 (D)
Anh. 97 (f#)
Anh. 98 (d)
Anh. 99 (d)
Anh. 100 (d)

Anh. 101 (g)
Anh. 102 (eb)
Anh. 103 (a)
Anh. 104 (c)
Anh. 105 (Bb)
Anh. 106 (g)

Selected Bibliography

*The following list includes
only sources consulted for information
about recordings and record reviews.
It does not include
supplemental sources of information
about the organs, performers, or composers.*

The American Organist. See *Music/The AGO and RCCO Magazine.*

Ars organi, vols. 52-60. Berlin: Merseburger, 1977-79.

Bielefelder Katalog: Klassik. 10 vols. Bielefeld: Bielefelder Verlaganstallt; Karlsruhe: G. Braun, 1971-80.

Coover, James B., and Richard Colvig. *Medieval and Renaissance Music on
Long-Playing Records.* Detroit Studies in Music Bibliography, 6. Detroit:
Information Coordinators, 1964.

Coover, James B., and Richard Colvig. *Supplement, 1962-71.* Detroit Studies
in Music Bibliography, 26. Detroit: Information Coordinators, 1973.

Deutsche Bibliographie: Schallplatten Verzeichnis. 4 vols. Bielefeld: Bielefelder
Verlaganstallt, 1975-78.

Diapason, vols. 67-71. Des Plaines, formerly Chicago: Scranton Gillette Com-
munications, 1976-80.

Diapason: Catalogue générale. 9 vols. Boulogne: Diapason, 1972-80.

Gemeinschaftskatalog '72/'73. Starnberg: Josef Keller (in cooperation with the
Bundesverband der Phonographischen Wirtschaft, Hamburg), 1973. The
same, '76/'77 (published 1977).

Gramophone Classical Catalogue, vols. 80-109. Kenton, Middlesex: General Gramo- phone Publications, 1973-80.

Gray, Michael, and Gerald Gibson. *Bibliography of Discographies I: Classical Music, 1925-1975.* New York: R. R. Bowker, 1977.

Grosse Schallplatten Katalog 1970. Ludenscheid: Carl v. d. Linnepe, 1970. 2. Nachtrag [supplement], 1970.

Hendrie, Gerald. *The Baroque Organ.* Milton Keynes: Open University Press, 1974.

Laade, Wolfgang. *Klangdokumente historischer Tasteninstrumente: Orgeln, Kiel- u. Hammerklaviere.* Zurich: Pelikan, 1972.

Maleady, Antoinette A. *Record and Tape Reviews Index, 1971-74.* 4 vols. Metuchen, NJ: Scarecrow Press, 1972-75.

Maleady, Antoinette A. *Index to Record and Tape Reviews, 1975-77.* 3 vols. San Anselmo, CA: Chulainn Press, 1976-78.

Music/The AGO and RCCO Magazine (beginning with the issue of January 1979, renamed *The American Organist*), vols. 9-13. New York: American Guild of Organists, 1975-79.

Musical Heritage Society Catalogue. 12 vols. Tinton Falls, NJ: Musical Heritage Society, 1970-82.

Musik und Kirche, vols. 45-50. Kassel: Bärenreiter, 1975-80.

Organ Literature Foundation: Catalogues L-N. Braintree, MA: Henry Karl Baker & Son, n. d.

Organ Yearbook, vols. 1-10. Buren, The Netherlands: Frits Knuf, 1970-79.

Perrault, André. *André Perrault International: Classical Records and Cassettes.* 3 vols. St.-Hyacinthe, Quebec: Les Editions Adagio, 1978-80.

Records in Review. 11 vols. Great Barrington, MA: Wyeth Press, 1967-77.

Bibliography

Schäfer, Ernst. *Laudatio organi: Eine Orgelfahrt von d. Ostsee bis z. Erzgebirge.* Leipzig: Deutscher Verlag für Musik, 1972.

Schallplatten Jahrbuch: Klassik Auslese. Karlsruhe: G. Braun, 1973.

Schwann-1 Record and Tape Guide, vols. 30-32. Boston: W. Schwann, 1978-80.

References are to entry numbers in the discography.
The entries in this index are those of the city or village;
where information was available,
the church or hall is identified next as listed
either in bibliographical sources or on the record jacket.

Australia

Austria

Germany

Holland

272

Medemblik, Bonifaciuskerk   86-87, 693
Nieuw-Scheemda   369
Noordbroek, Hervormde Kerk   750
Noordwolde   87
Oosthuizen, Nederlands Hervormde Kerk   86-87
Osteel   146
Rotterdam: Goede Herdekerk   765; Laurenskerk   469, 538, 635, 767
Rysum   146
The Hague: Jacobskerk   701; Kloosterkerk   539
Uithuizen, Dutch Reformed Church   335, 369, 742, 746
Utrecht, Geertekerk   181
Zwolle, St. Michael's (Grote Kerk)   21, 335, 370, 436, 489, 525, 583, 593,
   597, 742, 746, 750

Hungary

Sarospatak   814
Sopron, St. George's Cathedral   532, 813

Ireland

Dublin, Trinity College   350

Italy

Bergamo, Santa Anna di Borgo Palazzo   63
Beronico   643
Bologna, San Petronio   62-63, 68, 74, 80, 642, 746
Bolzano   841
Borca di Cadore   68
Brescia: Cathedral   68; San Carlo   63, 72, 667, 746; San Giuseppe   78,
   673, 675; unidentified   665, 670
Florence, San Domenico di Prato   75-76, 659
Modena, San Bernardino di Carpi   68, 674
Parma, Roncole Verdi di Busseto   660
Pisogne   656
Ravenna, Chiesa del Carmine   63
Trieste, Istituto Pia Casa dei Poveri   663
Val Venosta, Churburg Castle   149
Venice: Antico Conservatorio dell' Ospedaletto   65; Santa Maria del Riposo
   647; San Marco   651; unidentified   643

Toledo, OH, Collingwood Presbyterian Church   286
Washington, DC: All Souls' Church   454; Reformation Lutheran
    Church   174
Williamsburg, VA, College of William and Mary   168

Wales

Mold, Flintshire, Parish Church   373

Miscellaneous Instruments

Bureau, cabinet, and chamber organs   16, 29, 33, 134, 181
Claviorgana   152, 846
House organ   463
Portatives   1, 8
Positives   8, 10-12, 19, 23, 61, 83, 134, 141, 145, 148, 159, 183, 478, 829, 856
Regals   8, 14, 36, 134, 141
Secrétaire   134
Table organs   11, 131, 134

References are to entry numbers in the discography.
In mixed anthologies which include a variety of music performed
by two or more organists, only those who perform music
within the chronological limits of this study are included.
Names of other instrumentalists, singers, and ensembles are not listed.

Sanger, David   580
Saorgin, René   72, 222-23, 257, 263.2, 302, 311, 401-3, 597, 607, 618, 652-53, 672-73, 734, 756
Schäfer, Johannes   451
Scheidegger, Rudolf   840
Scheller, Helmut   780
Schipper, Fokke   404
Schmid, Anton   405
Schnauffer, Heinz   406, 815, 841
Schneider, Martin Gotthard   408
Schneider, Michael   407, 632
Schnoor, Hans T.   394
Schönstedt, Arno   409-10, 581, 590
Schoof, Armin   450
Schoonbroodt, Hubert   92, 615, 685, 692, 759
Schröder, Andreas   57, 400
Schuba, Konrad Philipp   411, 476, 654
Schuster, Hanns-Christoph   641
Schwarb, Egon   412, 779
Sebestyen, Janos   93
Sibertin-Blanc, Antoine   730
Sidwell, Martindale   33
Siedel, Mathias   344, 646, 655
Sluys, Jozef   686-87, 694-96
Smith, Melville   258, 309
Smith, Richard Birney   842
Soddemann, Fritz   413, 843
Spinelli, Gianfranco   68, 74
Stadtmüller, Peter Alexander   414, 844
Stender, Ernst-Erich   394
Stockmeier, Wolfgang   613, 845
Stoffers, Erich   414.1
Stricker, André   582
Syré, Wolfram   415
Szathmary, Zsigmond   535, 583

Tachezi, Herbert   161.1, 186, 416-18
Tagliavini, Luigi   68, 642, 656, 674-75
Talsma, Willem R.   87
Tambyeff, Raphael   259
Taylor, Frank   260, 320

PERFORMERS

References are to entry numbers in the discography.
In mixed anthologies which include music from different historical periods,
only those composers whose style falls within the chronological limits
of this study are included, and only music performed on the
organ as a solo instrument is included. Boldface type indicates
either complete works or anthologies of the works of the composer.

288